£1-95

THE INSTITUTE FOR PSYCHICAL RESEARCH

Hitherto unpublished accounts from their scientific files

GHOSTWATCH

Edited by Prof. Colin B. Gardner

THE INSTITUTE FOR PSYCHICAL RESEARCH

Hitherto unpublished accounts from their scientific files

GHOSTWATCH

Edited by Prof. Colin B. Gardner

foulsham

LONDON . NEW YORK . TORONTO . SYDNEY

foulsham

Yeovil Road, Slough, Berkshire SL1 4JH

ISBN 0–572–01549–6

Printed in Great Britain at St Edmundsbury Press, Bury St Edmunds

Contents

Introduction

A WORD OF WARNING. It has been an important consideration of The Institute for Psychical Research throughout its existence that it has no involvement in the increasing abuse of such a generally misunderstood subject as the paranormal. There are many people who would not hesitate to take advantage of this situation and readers are therefore warned to be wary of imitators, for reasons which will become obvious.

When The Institute for Psychical Research (IPR) was formed in 1960, the intention was to search for a hidden formula, which seemed to have eluded psychical researchers for centuries. It was the dawn of a new era, as young vibrant minds discussed unique ideas with a bold determination to find consistency in an area of research notorious for its inconsistencies.

IPR started from nothing; building up new trains of thought, lines of enquiry and methods of detection. It is no wonder such tools as these brought about a new scientific principle, which unfurled with time to form parascience — the science of the paranormal. The new science had to be tested to ensure that the results of investigations would not simply fall apart a year later, as many previous results had been known to do. However, parascience has stood the test of time for almost thirty years, and has expanded and become more and more exacting as new technologies were scavenged from other scientific doctrines. The newborn parascience succeeded finally in dragging psychical research out of the dark ages and into the twentieth century, at least within the confines of The Institute for Psychical Research.

From the scientific criteria of parascience came a growing reputation, trust and respect, which has never before been attributed to psychical research; with it, a growing hunger has come for factual knowledge, from both professional investigators and amateurs.

With no desire for publicity-seeking sensationalism, IPR has worked quietly on, in much the same way as any other scientific research establishment, restricted from answering the many leading authorities in their pleas for the knowledge gained through serious psychical research. Those pleas, however, were noted.

The fruits of serious research have paid off and the benefits derived from parascience have been enormous, in terms of satisfactory, professional investigations, as well as the tremendous scope of subjects and phenomena to be studied. Even in the 1970s, it was possible to authenticate a haunting from the scientifically formulated investigation of a single report from a mere child — a situation which other researchers have repeatedly given a wide berth. Only now, over a decade later, is the legal system in Britain accepting testimony from children as witnesses in selected cases.

Today, The Institute for Psychical Research, having left all antiquated beliefs far behind, is preparing to launch into the twenty-first century, still young, vibrant and determined in its effective search for truth and fact.

The search itself can take many forms, and be either simple, complex, or anything between the two extremes. An unsubstantiated report can be confirmed many years later by an unexpected telephone call from a witness previously unheard of, or what is considered to be a definite haunting can have researchers labouring over old documents trying to find some elusive proof of an important aspect in the case.

In general, an investigation is conducted in a manner which is not dissimilar to a criminal investigation by the police. This may not be obvious to discern because of the different methods used to determine the facts, and it is not unusual for a percipient to be confused by the obscure relevance of certain questions and indeed the whole investigation. But unlike the police, our methods are only available to our own scientific community and are not generally available.

To understand the value of this, let us consider the thief who is unaware of the use of fingerprints in police work. That thief is unlikely to wear gloves and the police would have an improved chance of catching the culprit. A closer example to our own techniques is the motorist who is unaware of police radar. When stopped and informed that the speed limit was being exceeded, the motorist may be completely surprised that the police can tell the exact speed of the vehicle. These police techniques are, however, public knowledge, and it is fair to say that many people are deterred from crime because of this general knowledge about crime detection methods. Unfortunately, the thief in our example is now likely to wear gloves, thus lessening the chance of capture, but nevertheless this knowledgeable criminal is anticipated to represent a minority and so a greater public good is served.

The paranormal is a different subject entirely, and while the knowledge of our techniques would serve the public from an educational standpoint, it is not likely to deter any frauds. Instead, inexperienced people would then use carefully validated techniques and misinterpret them, thereby adding more confusion to the subject in general, and causing significantly more harm than good.

The easiest aspect to understand about psychical research is that while investigations should be conducted with the professionalism of a police investigation, some differences of approach are inevitable because of the substantial difference between the natural world and that of the supernatural.

One important consideration in any investigation, is obviously the testimony of a witness. The complexities of the paranormal made it necessary for parascience to find a solution to the problem of assessing the truthfulness of testimonies. But it is not quite as simple as that because in some situations a witness may truly have seen a ghost, yet there is no proof of a haunting. Therefore, the truth alone cannot be relied upon. Having said that, a witness's testimony can be of the utmost importance, as it alone may sometimes provide the vital proof required for a decision about authenticity to be made, regardless of whether the account itself is true or false.

The evidence may be either nonexistent or insurmountable in any given case, but lack of evidence does not mean there is no haunting, just as an abundance of evidence cannot be taken as categorical proof of a haunting. The investigating officers have to assess the truth and any available evidence, to provide a report which proves beyond a doubt what the facts of the case are. The business of confirming or denying the existence of an actual haunting is far from being a simple one.

What makes an investigation more complicated is that, basically, every haunting is unique. By that I mean the components which make up the phenomena are rarely the same in each case. Therefore the guidelines for one investigated haunting can be entirely different from the guidelines applying to another, as what is 'normal' in one case could easily be impossible in another similar case. In light of this, even the outer casing of an investigation may be adapted to the requirements of individual cases, and percipients may be descended upon by anything from a hard-line international group of investigators with a van full of equipment, to the friendly, local team of Ghostbusters — yes, they really do exist, though not in the same guise as their megastar counterparts of the film world, much to the disappointment of some percipients, I might add. Whatever the method of investigation, parascience allows no deviation from the central core of strict scientific principles.

With such fluid phenomena, one would not expect to find cases which could be described as typical. However, such cases do exist, but only because it is currently impossible to completely define the factors that make the cases unique. The most prevalent and all-time classical haunting is one which is rarely read about, and rarely reported, yet there are estimated to be well over a million such hauntings in Britain alone, that is of a ghost seen, felt, or otherwise sensed as it moves through the room of someone's home, etcetera. While many residents affected by such a haunting either do not believe in its existence or are not aware of it, others accept the presence in just the same way as they do the roofs above their heads. Enquiries thus far have revealed little information about such hauntings, but there is no denying their existence, although they can be most difficult to prove.

It would seem then, that an individual cannot be expected to know if he or she has experienced a haunting. But such a surmise would be inaccurate. The truth is that a person may or may not be aware. An individual who is not aware of a haunting is obviously not going to report it; but one who is aware, should be encouraged to record immediately the event exactly as it occurred, and then report it. Under no circumstances should information either be added or deleted in order to make the phenomena more believable or interesting — such is not important; facts are! There is no ridicule in the parascientific world for believing there to be a haunting, whether the report is proven or not.

The cases I have selected for this book will illustrate many of the above points, and are excellent examples of hauntings scientifically proven beyond doubt. All are unique in some way, and represent a rare opportunity for readers to gain a fascinating insight into the *real* supernatural world.

IPR's excellent reputation has resulted in the willingness of individuals to share even their most private moments, without fear, and for this immeasurable thanks are given. I express my thanks also to everyone throughout the world who has made this book possible.

C.B.G.

Doomed To Walk
This Way

The way in which a haunting is reported can often be fascinating in itself. In this first case, it was by a chance encounter, which belied the actual trauma suffered over the previous twelve months. It was even more bizarre because it was reported by a man who did not believe in ghosts and had never seen the one he reported. Confused by the events around him at home and terrified of public ridicule, Bob was perhaps cruelly thrust by fate into a situation that compelled him to speak out about a subject at which he would previously have scoffed.

BOB AND KATHY loved their modern new home. The attractive, semi-detached bungalow boasted, among other notable features, an immaculate, long, rear garden which was separated from the open fields beyond by an old hawthorn hedge. Being set in a quiet, rural village near Preston, Lancashire, the location itself exuded an air of peace and tranquility.

The couple had no interest in the paranormal, nor had either of them experienced anything remotely connected with psychic phenomena, hence, they could never have perceived beforehand the strange visitations they had inherited.

Within a short time of moving into the bungalow, their serenity was disrupted by the occasional, but nevertheless disconcerting ghost of a young man repeatedly and inexplicably walking through their garden.

The first time Kathy noticed the occurrence, she described the sighting as more of a shadow crossing the kitchen window which overlooked the driveway. It prompted her to look up inquisitively from washing the dishes. As she watched, the form became more distinct and she could clearly see it was a young man. He wore old, brown, cord trousers, a dirty-grey jacket which sagged at the pockets through long years of misuse, and a pair of tough shoes, splattered with dried mud and lacking the shine of polish. His clothes did not appear to be of a different era, as they were not unlike those worn by many of the local youths who worked on the surrounding farms. Indeed, in his solidity, he could easily have passed for such.

11

Kathy was non-plussed. Why was this young stranger coming to her back door? Then, from the rear kitchen window, she saw the young man slowly and smoothly march through the garden towards the hawthorn hedge. She quickly dried her hands and rushed outside, but there was no sign of him.

As weeks went by, Kathy saw this sequence of events repeated several times.

The apparition always took the same path alongside the bungalow, rounding the back as if coming to knock at the back door. He walked with his head low, his eyes to the ground. But instead of coming to the door, he would turn away from the bungalow and stride steadily towards the bottom of the lush garden. He continued in a straight line still with his head down, never looking at anything he passed, seemingly preoccupied and oblivious to anyone watching. Passing easily through the thick hawthorn hedge and out into the middle of the adjoining field, he would stop momentarily before vanishing.

Frequently, his form would become faintly visible only at some point in the garden, as if he had appeared out of nowhere to continue just the final leg of his homogeneous journey. Or he would appear suddenly, solid and real, passing the kitchen window that looked out on the driveway. There was no routine of appearance and disappearance, for he also sometimes disappeared before reaching his destination in the field. However, he was always dressed the same way, adopted an unvarying mournful appearance and kept exactly to his scheduled route throughout.

Like most mothers, Kathy did not mention the unusual presence to her two young children, as she had no wish to alarm them about a situation which she could not herself explain. When she finally told her husband, Bob, she found him sceptical but understanding, though he was always busy with something else when the sightings took place, and never able to arrive in time to catch even a glimpse when Kathy called him to come and see the ghostly figure.

Kathy was beginning to doubt her own sanity, for there was no one to confirm the visions that she saw and, no matter how she tried to put it out of her mind, the young man persisted in his lonely walk through the garden every two or three days. Sometimes it seemed one journey was not enough, and he would complete it again and again; up to seven times Kathy counted in a single day.

One Sunday afternoon, Kathy's parents came to visit. As they departed from their car at the kerbside, they both noticed a young man walking along the drive towards the bungalow. They were mildly surprised because they had not seen him earlier, and wondered where he could have appeared from. They opened the driveway gate and followed the man towards the rear of the bungalow.

The back door, which opened into the dining room, was ajar. On reaching it, Betty peered cautiously inside, not wanting to intrude on her daughter's other visitor. The family were sitting at the dining table, Bob and Kathy busily talking and drinking coffee as the children finished their lunch.

Knocking on the door, Betty tentatively walked in followed by her husband, Harold. After the usual family greetings had been exchanged, Betty quietly asked Kathy who their other visitor was. Kathy and Bob looked at each other with obvious confusion, both waiting for the other to answer. Bob eventually told her there *was* no other visitor.

Betty viewed him with disbelief. She was concerned by his unexpected reply and, as soon as the children ran out to play in the garden, she went on to explain that both Harold and herself definitely followed a young man along the drive, and saw him distinctly until he rounded the corner of the bungalow ahead of them. They assumed, naturally, that he had arrived at the back door and entered just moments before they did, and were confused to find that he was not in the dining room with them. Betty described the young man. Her description, substantiated by her husband, fitted exactly the strange young man Kathy had so frequently seen.

Kathy was comforted in that she had not imagined the stranger, yet she was more convinced than ever before that what she had seen was in fact a ghost.

However, as time went by, Kathy's temporary consolation was soon to be replaced by her earlier doubts about her sanity when she realised the ghostly presence had not been seen since that Sunday afternoon. She thought it might be possible for the haunting to cease, having now been confirmed by a third party, but found she could not, in all honesty, accept that explanation. She questioned her parents many times in an effort to understand why — as she had certainly not imagined the young man — had he suddenly stopped appearing. Kathy also started to spend more time in the kitchen, where she had the best view of the drive at the side of the bungalow as well as seeing a good portion of the back garden, but still the mysterious visitor never came.

As the months went by, however, the young ghost became more of a distant memory.

One morning, as Kathy stood at the rear kitchen window, gazing admiringly at the beautiful garden flowers, he was suddenly there, casually walking past the window as if his last visit had been just yesterday!

The shock was painful.

She could have cursed the ghostly figure that had caused her so much mental anguish before. And now, almost a year later, he was back!

Three days after the spectre's return, Kathy and her parents were sitting talking and enjoying the warm October sun on the sheltered patio extending from the rear of the bungalow, when the young man suddenly and silently appeared from the driveway.

Apparently unaware of anyone, he proceeded down the garden, as usual, staring at the ground. Betty shouted to him, but he took no notice. Spontaneously, Kathy and her mother rose with alacrity and hurried after him. Only a few seconds later did Kathy wonder what they proposed to do if they did in fact catch him. But he was now nearing the bottom of the long garden and by the time the two women reached the hawthorn hedge, he had arrived at his usual destination in the field and disappeared.

Predictably, now he was back, several more sightings were experienced during October.

Kathy was almost getting accustomed to the sudden appearance of this lonely entity. So when she caught a glimpse of him one morning, without a second thought she rapped on the kitchen window; then stood back aghast! Would cold, grey eyes rise to meet her own frozen stare in a challenging response? Would he pass through the brick wall as easily as he did the hawthorn hedge? Or would he merely vanish like a fading shadow?

But no. The loud rapping might not have existed, for he deviated not the slightest from his customary gait as he continued the ghostly ritual.

Bob hardly knew what to do; one minute his wife was totally sceptical and explaining away the visions as a trick of the light, and the next, she was adamant that it could be nothing but a ghost. Bob found himself following her lead by agreeing with her constantly fluctuating opinion.

Even if nothing else was clear, it soon became apparent that this visitation was to be seen only during the month of October, and it would seem, *every* October.

A solution to their quandary came quite unexpectedly by way of a chance encounter in a local pub one Sunday. Bob was having a lunchtime drink with his golfing partner, Chris. They had just finished a couple of rounds at the golf course and the topic of conversation was of course, golf.

Then Chris noticed an old friend ordering a drink and called for him to come and join them. George, an investigator with The Institute for Psychical Research, came and sat down; and, as one might expect, the introductions alone inevitably changed the topic of conversation from golf to ghosts.

Bob was becoming increasingly uncomfortable. Here he was, sitting next to someone who actually investigates ghosts, and back at home, one could be walking through his garden at that very moment. In his dilemma, Bob was bursting to tell all, yet terrified of seeing his name splashed across the front page of every newspaper, quickly followed by the constant barrage of reporters who would arrive from anywhere and everywhere to pound on his front door from morning till night. On top of this, he did not even believe in ghosts. Neither, he was sure, did Chris.

Bob was wrong on both counts. Much later, he was to discover not only a complete lack of newspaper reporters, but also that Chris and George had met two years previously during an investigation at Chris' place of work.

It was at least twenty minutes before Bob, having studied George carefully in his censored replies to Chris' endless questions, started to ask his own. And finally, he told his story and asked for help.

The ensuing investigation began with a check into the background of the bungalow, discovering that there had been numerous owners considering it was not that old. The longest time an occupant had lived there was a little over three and a half years. Most stayed just a year.

Investigating further back before the bungalow was built, revealed that the land had been part of a farm, to which the field at the rear still belonged. A path was discovered which corresponded exactly to the ghost's movements across the family's garden, through a one-time gap in the hawthorn hedge, and into the field, where in the middle was once a pond.

Being October, there was no difficulty in confirming that the haunting was real, though it was the farm at the rear from which an explanation emerged.

The couple at the farm had a son late in life. They did not want their boy to continue working the land, but instead encouraged him to study hard at school so that he might have a better start in life. This he did, earning himself a place at a university.

But after a while, he became troubled by something and, between studying, he would often walk the path around the fields with his head down, as if trying to make some difficult decision. The young farmer's parents were concerned about his isolation, but he would not talk of his worry, and they could do nothing but sympathetically watch as he walked alone; and hope that he might find a solution to whatever depressed him so much. The young man never deviated from the path, except for one solemn afternoon in October, when he stopped by the pond and for reasons known only to himself, leapt into the murky water and drowned.

Since that time, it seems he is destined to return each year in October during the weeks leading up to the anniversary of his death, and following his own footsteps to the point which marks the end of his mortal life.

Bob and Kathy have since sold their bungalow, adding to the long list of owners who perhaps could not live with their annual visits from the ghostly farmer who is doomed to walk this way.

Ghost-Sitting

Despite Jackie's ordeal, it was almost a year later when this case came to light, and even then, it was by way of casual conversation about strange events, with a group of friends. It was only indirectly from this that The Institute for Psychical Research came to hear of the haunting, and considerable work was entailed in tracing the matter back to Jackie. The next line of enquiry was directed to the couple involved, but they knew nothing of their apartment being haunted, and suggested that we had come to the wrong address as they were not interested in occult matters. Nevertheless, they finally agreed to give us the names of some of their recent babysitters. Before long, we had returned for a more comprehensive list and to ask if they would allow us to conduct an investigation. An unusual aspect was presented in the sheer number of witnesses who echoed Jackie's statement about the haunting, while the couple themselves had no idea of the real cause of their difficulty in retaining a babysitter. It was perhaps hardly surprising the couple were so blissfully unaware of the haunting, as they were at work each time it occurred.

MOST PEOPLE WOULD agree that Jackie Andrews, in her late twenties, was a lively, intelligent young woman, not given to flights of fancy or bouts of over-imagination. She had an interest in the paranormal, and had often been told by clairvoyants and mediums alike, that she was psychic. Jackie felt in no position to dispute this, as she had often heard noises others around her had not heard, and had experienced many precognitive dreams. None of these prepared Jackie for the events of the month of June which she is not likely, ever to forget.

It began, as many things often do, in a simple way. Jackie was asked by a married couple she knew fairly well, but not intimately, if she would do a few hours babysitting. Jackie agreed. The couple were in show business, and often worked during the evenings. Their luxury apartment, which Jackie had never been to before, was situated in a quiet residential area of London, Ontario. The apartment reflected the years in the entertainment business which had brought sufficient wealth and many fond memories to the couple as well as their avid appreciation of fine art, sculpture and the most unusual bric-à-brac.

Jackie arrived at the appointed time, and amid the distracting beauty of the apartment, she was shown where everything was kept and told to help herself to any food or drink that she might require during the evening.

The couple's little boy was no trouble at all, being in bed when Jackie arrived and he slept the whole of the time she was there. She was grateful for this because, from the moment she entered the elegant dwelling, Jackie was also overwhelmed by a tense feeling of oppression which she tried to brush aside as the evening wore on.

Not being able to settle in the spacious living room, Jackie moved to the dining room, then to the kitchen; back to the living room again, then the kitchen. So it progressed all evening, twenty minutes one room, half an hour another and so on. The walls seemed to close in on her, and the couple's poodle would suddenly start howling for no apparent reason. Darting about the room snarling and growling, it persistently jumped up to snap at something in the air which proved fearfully invisible to Jackie's eyes and other senses.

Making a coffee in the kitchen, Jackie felt the hairs bristle on the back of her neck. She was positive she was being watched and followed, but she could see no one.

She looked in on the little boy several times, worried that he might awaken similarly terrified if he also sensed the dank atmosphere which now dominated the apartment. But he slept peacefully, apparently unaware of his guardian's dilemma.

The very air was heavy, foul smelling and cloying. It seemed to heave at Jackie as she tried to remain calm. She wanted desperately to leave but dared not abandon her charge. At last, the couple returned home and Jackie virtually fled the place.

Despite this harrowing experience, Jackie surprised herself by agreeing, a few days later, to babysit again.

Once more, she had barely entered the luxurious apartment when the atmosphere became foul and heavy again. The couple had only just left and she wanted to chase after them, to tell them she must leave. But how could she expect the couple to cancel their engagement at such short notice, and simply on the grounds of her intangible fear? She submitted to her promise and settled on the sofa with a magazine, in the hope that she could distract herself in its glossy pages.

The little boy slept undisturbed, but the poodle started its snarling and barking ritual, head high in the air, teeth bared and making the most ghastly howling.

17

Jackie again felt as if she was being watched and followed as she moved to the kitchen to make herself a cup of coffee. Whenever she moved, whatever she did, she could feel the oppression following, watching, stalking her without reprieve.

Not only was the atmosphere redolent of stale odour and dank decay, it felt positively evil and menacing. There was nothing to account for this smell. The carpet and much of the furniture were new, and the apartment was kept in a pristine condition.

Just after midnight, the phenomena became worse.

Sitting on the edge of a plush easy chair, Jackie suddenly heard the distinct melancholy ticking of an old clock, as if one had been suspended in mid-air a few inches from her face. The poodle immediately dashed in and started its terrified howling, barking and snarling again, jumping into the air directly in front of Jackie's chair, as if trying to expel the unearthly clock from the apartment.

Fearing for her sanity if she were to remain there alone, Jackie hastily phoned her husband, Alan. He more or less said it was all nonsense but reluctantly agreed to come over.

When he arrived, Jackie was too frightened to leave the security of the easy chair and so shouted to Alan that the door was unlocked. On hearing him enter, Jackie called out that she was in the living room.

A couple of endless minutes past.

Jackie was about to call out again, when Alan appeared in the doorway looking perplexed. After a moment, he enquired, 'Does the chandelier in the entry hall usually spin round like that?'

Jackie stared at him. Was he joking? Ridiculing her? She pleaded with him not to tease, and stressed that she was not imagining the atmosphere or the strange smells or the presence of something evil.

'I am not joking!' said Alan. 'Come and look!'

Jackie gripped his arm tightly and followed him into the entry hall where a large ornamental chandelier was spinning round, first one way, then the other. They both stood petrified, hardly believing their eyes.

When it finally stopped, they virtually tripped over one another in their haste to seek the dubious sanctuary of the living room. They huddled together on the sofa, breathing in the heavy, foul atmosphere with nerves cringing, as the dog began howling and snapping again.

When the couple returned, Jackie hurriedly dragged Alan from the apartment telling the couple she could *never* babysit there again!

Phantom Mechanic

This particular case, reported by a neighbour, required special consideration in its investigation, due to the fact that the main percipients could not be approached immediately, for reasons that will be made obvious. Their neighbour, Mrs C., already knew of our reputation and would not have reported the haunting to anyone else. She knew that our interest in the phenomena would not override feelings of compassion, and so felt obliged to talk to us when she saw at the house across the road, a ghost leaving the front door and passing through the closed garage door. Most of the investigation was conducted in the form of a surveillance, operating from a caravan in the drive of Mrs C.'s home. It was one of the those rare instances in which we were able to gather information about the haunting as it progressed, although the case is portrayed here from the viewpoint of the main percipients who had no prior knowledge of our presence at the location.

EVER SINCE HE was two years old, Martin had been fanatical about cars. It was therefore no surprise to his parents, Doug and Terry, when, at a time so many sixteen-year-olds were dashing out to buy their first means of transportation, the motorcycle, Martin announced that he intended to buy an old car. He had already found the car he wanted, a 1963 Ford Anglia which he planned to rebuild by his seventeenth birthday.

Having faithfully saved for this project, he had kept his eye on the decaying automobile for some eighteen months and had finally discussed a sale with its owner. All he required now was his parents' approval. Doug would need to park his car on the drive as there was only room for one car in the garage, and there was much work to be performed to bring the old Anglia up to standard again.

Doug and Terry were relieved, as many parents often are, that their son did not want a motorbike. However, much discussion was needed before finally agreeing to Martin's request. It was ultimately decided that Martin could have use of the garage for one year, as long as he did not lose interest in the project. The last thing Doug wanted was to be forced to keep his car on the drive while the garage was occupied by an abandoned, partly rebuilt, old car. The only other point that concerned Doug and Terry was whether Martin could actually regenerate the life in a car which had been barely looked at in five years, let alone had its engine cranked.

Arrangements were subsequently made to have the car brought to their home where it was pushed with great effort into the garage. It was in a terrible state. The tyres were flat, the body rusted, crumpled and scratched. It had stiff doors, broken trim, torn upholstery, seized brakes, half of the roof lining was hanging down and the engine was caked in an oily gunge. The engine compartment provided a home for at least a dozen spiders, and several more had taken up residence in the car's interior.

It was a mystery how anyone could be enthralled by such a pitiful sight, but Martin was. He could not have been more elated if his parents had bought him the latest Ferrari model.

Fortunately, Martin's new job as an apprentice mechanic was going to be beneficial in his ambitious hobby, as the two were unquestionably complementary to each other.

Every evening after dinner, Martin would disappear to the garage where he would work for hours on his car. His parents had never seen him happier, with a smile on his face when he set off for work and wearing an even bigger smile when he returned. At weekends, he laboured over his pride and joy from morning till night, with only an occasional evening out with his friends, and, rarely, an outing at the weekend when he would go off for the day with his friend Stephen, returning to spend the remaining twilight hours working in the garage on his beloved car.

After about six months, Martin was well ahead on his schedule for rebuilding the Anglia. Stephen started to call more often and he and Martin would go out for the day on Stephen's motorbike. This worried Doug and Terry. They had hoped Martin's car would keep him away from motorbikes, but they did not want to start making demands that their son could not see his friend purely because he rode a motorbike. No, Martin had worked relentlessly, and they were proud of their son; no matter how much they disliked him riding motorbikes, at least it was only at weekends.

They also respected all those long, hard hours Martin had put into rebuilding his car and had to admit he deserved a break from it. After all, the car was now showing signs of being a working machine. Martin had brought home: exhaust, battery, wiring, hoses, newly chromed bumpers, renovated wheels fitted with new tyres, driving lights, seats, etc. So much had he brought, that his parents wondered if he was building a second car.

By May, some ten months into Martin's project, the Ford Anglia looked a completely different car. Not a spot of rust anywhere; a complete respray and regular cleaning by Martin had the body shining like a new pin. All the engine had been stripped down, cleaned, parts replaced where necessary, and reconstructed, adding a few up-to-date extras. The electrical system was still causing problems, but Martin was confident he could solve that. There was no auto electrician at work to ask advice from, but he had some books for reference, so was sure the Anglia would be running by his seventeenth birthday just two months away.

Stephen had arrived on his motorbike every Saturday afternoon. Martin would dash out with his crash helmet, jump on the back of Stephen's bike and they would speed off down the road.

It was one such Saturday afternoon, just as Terry was preparing the dinner, when the police arrived to inform them of an accident involving Stephen's bike. Stephen was critically ill in hospital. Martin had been killed.

The next four weeks passed in a kind of oblivion for Doug and Terry. Perhaps it was the lack of Martin's familiar banging from the garage that brought them back to reality. It was only now that they could brave themselves to talk about their tragedy and try to continue with their lives.

They discussed whether to take the holiday they had booked. In two weeks, both of them were due to fly to Spain for a week. Martin had wanted to stay at home so he could finish the car. The car! What on earth were they going to do about Martin's car? Doug suggested they could sell it; it was almost completed, except for the wiring problem and possibly adjustments to the engine once it was running. But he could not seriously consider selling Martin's car; it would be akin to an act of sacrilege. The now gleaming Anglia was almost like a monument to Martin's skill and dedication. How could they part with it? Terry certainly would not hear of it, and she said so. With that decision, they sank back into oblivion for several more days.

It was only the urgency of their impending holiday that interrupted their mourning. At this time, they had both been vaguely aware of banging and shuffling sounds coming from the garage during the last three evenings. It was a comforting, familiar sound, and one they had lived with to the point of accustomed detachment.

They were both struck by the realisation that it could not have been Martin, for he was dead. But as soon as they became certain the noises were real, they stopped.

The following evening they listened intently for the sounds they knew so well.

Shortly before eight o'clock, they heard a faint metallic tapping and some scraping noises. Terry broke down in tears, while Doug dashed out to the garage.

He was just unlocking the garage door when he heard the unmistakable sound of a spanner being dropped on the concrete floor inside. He quickly turned the handle and lifted the up-and-over door. The garage was in darkness.

Doug switched on the light, not knowing what to expect. There was no sound as he tentatively entered alongside his son's car. He searched the garage, but there was no one there. The car's bonnet was up, and he thought this strange, as Martin usually closed it when he was not working on the engine, but the last few weeks had left his mind in a fog, and now he was not sure if Martin may have left it open. Doug looked into the shining engine compartment to see if any tools had been left on top of the engine. He also looked over every part of the floor, but there was no spanner, or any other stray tools to be found.

Martin was meticulous about his tools, they were always put away in his toolbox which Doug found sitting neatly on the workbench, its lid closed. Doug noticed underneath the workbench, Martin's other toolbox which had been returned from his place of work. Its lid was also closed. It served to remind Doug that the car's bonnet had indeed been closed when he put the second toolbox underneath the bench.

Doug closed the bonnet, not sure if it was out of respect for his dead son, or as an attempt to stop the hurtful reminder the noises brought of that tragic day.

The noises continued each evening, however. At any time between six-thirty and nine o'clock, they would begin: either the sound of a hammer banging heavily, or tapping lightly, sounds of a ratchet tool being turned, a car door slamming, the very sounds which evoked with painful clarity the hours of devotion and dexterity Martin had spent on that car.

Each time when the noises began, Doug would go to investigate but find nothing.

Again, in desperation, he suggested selling the Anglia, but Terry was against it, even though the ghostly sounds from the garage each evening upset her so much that she was now washed out from crying herself to sleep every night.

It was here decided that they should take their holiday, to get away for a short time, and perhaps they would see the situation more clearly on their return.

The week in Spain had been beneficial to both, they were able to relax for the first time since Martin's death. They were not fully recovered, but at least felt more at ease and more rested.

They had not been back in the house five minutes when their next-door neighbour knocked at the door. She was confused and distraught. She had come to tell them of the bizarre events going on in the garage while they were away.

As the homely, forty-year-old neighbour related those all-too-familiar sounds, it brought a constricting swell to their throats. Not

22

only had the noises been much louder, lights had been switched on and off both in the garage and the house. The racket had been so loud and had gone on for so long that it was at first thought someone was feverishly trying to finish the work on Martin's car in time for his birthday. Then, because whoever it was seemed to have the full run of the house, it was assumed Doug had cancelled the holiday to finish the car himself. Finally when none of these explanations made sense, the police had been called out, three times in all, to check for an intruder. The officers were quite baffled, as the noises had already stopped by the time they arrived. The last time they were called out, they found the garage light on, but there was no sign of a forced entry and all they could see through the small garage window was Martin's car with the bonnet open.

Doug was one hundred per cent certain the bonnet was closed when they left for Spain, and with that, all three marched defiantly to the garage. Doug opened the door to find the bonnet closed. On closer inspection, he discovered both of Martin's toolboxes were now on the top of the workbench, neatly sitting side by side, with their lids closed.

The next few nights were quiet. It was only by chance when their neighbour asked Terry if Doug had resorted to keeping a vigil in the garage, that they were made aware of the garage light being on for several hours each evening.

When the day of Martin's birthday arrived. Doug was too upset to go to work. The couple spent the day comforting each other until they were alarmed by what sounded like a car engine starting up in the garage. They rushed out and threw open the garage door to find the Anglia with its engine running.

They stood there in astonishment for several minutes before Doug uneasily crept alongside the car. He carefully opened the driver's door, and reached inside for the ignition key to switch off the engine, but the key was not there! He immediately looked to the workbench and there, hanging on a hook, were the car keys.

Unsure of what to do, he retreated to the house and phoned the local garage to send someone out.

Terry was transfixed at the garage entrance, tears and mascara running down her face. Doug tried to take her inside the house, but she would not move, and started to scream hysterically at his attempts. Resigned to his lack of control over the situation, he held her close and waited for the arrival of the mechanic.

For some fifteen minutes, the Anglia's engine purred like that of a new car. Then unexpectedly, it started to falter, splutter, cough, and finally it chugged to a halt. Terry thought she saw Martin at the back of the garage just prior to this, and heard his voice through the drone of the engine saying: 'Look Mum, I've done it!' But due perhaps to the blur of her tear-filled eyes, and shock at the bizarre event, she wondered if it was just a trick of her tired imagination.

Less than five minutes later, the mechanic from the local garage arrived.

On hearing the details and seeing the distress of Terry, the mechanic assured them he would make the car safe. He checked under the bonnet and inside the car, explaining that it must have been started by a short circuit in the ignition wires. He told Doug the fuel tank was a quarter-full and if the engine was running so well, he could not understand why it should stop like that.

Doug was not sure about a short circuit causing the car to start. It was the ignition wires Martin was having trouble with, and as far as Doug was aware, some of the wires were not even connected, for they and the choke cable could be plainly seen hanging from a hook near the workbench.

Whatever the cause, the garage was quiet after that day.

Much later, the couple decided to sell the Anglia to Gary, one of Martin's friends. After evaluating the work Martin had done, Gary discovered that he needed only to connect the ignition wires and choke cable to start up the car. Amazingly, the engine needed no adjustment, for it purred like that of a new car.

Doug and Terry now firmly believe the car was started by the ghost of their son, Martin. It was days later when they realised the significance of the car having started up at five minutes past two on the afternoon of their son's birthday, for it was the exact time that Martin was born.

The Haunted Toilet

In contrast to the previous case, this one was so pleasantly hilarious that it is a miracle any sense was made of the investigation. This type of case is regarded as a luxury after weeks of spending cold nights in isolated graveyards to no avail. Indeed, some of the investigators on this case went on to such a dismal prospect. The witnesses in the case had always ignored this most un-usual occurrence, and it was only when a new witness, Heather, came on the scene that this secret haunting was reported. Four days after Heather's arrival, the investi-gating team were positioned throughout the premises to record the phenomena. As the team were observers, no further reference has been made to their presence.

A HAUNTED TOILET may sound like a joke. But the staff of a well-known shoe shop in Preston, Lancashire, did not find it par-ticularly funny.

No one was certain for how long the phenomena had been going on. The shop's staff had remained unchanged for a good many years, and the disturbance was accepted as merely something odd, which happened occasionally.

Then, one of the staff retired. A young woman named Heather was immediately employed as a replacement. At this point the dis-turbance began to get out of hand.

No one had thought to mention the ghostly happenings to Heather. So, on Heather's second day in the shop, when she heard a female voice sharply call her name while she was sitting on the toilet, she thought nothing of it, merely assuming one of the girls was enquiring where she was. She called out that she would not be a minute. To her annoyance, the voice called her name again even more insistently: 'Heather! Heather!'

Hurrying out of the lavatory and into the staff room, Heather was surprised to see no one there. She entered the shop to find two of the girls serving customers, another in the office and yet another just returning from the shops with a new jar of coffee for the morning break.

At the first opportunity, Heather asked the girls who had needed her. Everyone looked blank. Then, Miss Rolstone, a kindly and mild-mannered spinster, informed Heather that it had probably been the resident ghost, who was in the habit of calling out for folk while they are tending the needs of nature in the lavatory, sometimes in an enquiring voice and sometimes in a sharp urgent tone. 'We are all used to it,' Miss Rolstone added.

Had anyone else mentioned this to Heather, she would have laughed and put it down to a joke being played on the 'new girl'. But Miss Rolstone was such a sensible, sincere person. Indeed, all the staff were of a responsible nature, who enjoyed their work and the companionship of their fellow workers.

The resident lady ghost had taken rather a fancy to Heather it seemed, or maybe considered the new girl as fresh sport, as hardly a day went by without something happening.

One afternoon, Heather was carefully replacing a shoe in the display window. It was a tricky business, as one had to climb into the window, then advance among the numerous, closely-grouped display stands with extreme caution to reach the required position to replace items without sending intricate displays crashing down all around. Heather was just about to back out when she received a none-too-delicate push. Clutching to save herself, she knocked over a tall display stand which wasted no time in proving the efficiency of the 'domino theory' by progressively demolishing most of the window display. 'For goodness sake!' Heather called out, and turning round to admonish whoever had climbed into the window and pushed her, she was shocked to find no one there. At a glance she could see the rest of the staff were indeed occupied, and Heather resigned herself to matching shoes with price tickets, and rebuilding the window display alone.

The next morning was a quiet one, so the girls took the opportunity to sit at the far end of the narrow shop and have a chat. Opposite the line of chairs where they settled, was a door leading down to the cellar.

The shop, though expensively and tastefully fitted out, was an extremely old premises with the cellar running the full length of the shop. The cellar was cold, damp, musty and creepy. Everyone hated having to go down there. This was thankfully rare, as the cellar housed only old pieces of carpet, about twenty chairs and several heavy window-display stands. It was the latter which were sometimes needed.

This particular morning there was no reason for anyone to go down into the cellar. All the staff were seated on the comfortable armchairs enjoying a rare, peaceful few minutes. So, it was no surprise that the girls all jumped and stared at one another when a strange noise echoed up from the depths of the cellar.

No one said a word. They all sat rigidly in their chairs, listening intently.

From below the floor, they heard display stands clatter and chair legs scrape across the stone floor, as if someone was rummaging around in a desperate attempt to find something.

One by one, the girls obstinately refused to go down to investigate.

Finally, the eldest and most senior member of staff, Mrs Clayman, a lady of a most down-to-earth nature and often formidable in terms of her disciplinary measures of the staff, and care of the shop, took charge of the matter and hurried down to the cellar. She had barely taken three strides down the stairs when the commotion stopped. Seconds later, two of the girls felt an icy blast of air rush past them, it was distinctly different from the feel of cold air when Mrs Clayman had opened the cellar door to descend the stone steps.

Speculation among the girls concluded that even the resident ghost feared the wrath of Mrs Clayman.

Heather, who found herself becoming interested in these strange occurrences, later asked Miss Rolstone if this noise from the cellar had happened before. Miss Rolstone told her it had, but never so conspicuously as it did that morning; the phenomena in the cellar had until then been dismissed as mice or wind, or even that someone (a member of the staff) was in the cellar, as often individuals would be busy with their own duties at the time.

A few days later, Heather was busy with a customer, and counting her blessings that she was not serving the elderly couple at the far end of the shop. Miss Rolstone was dealing with this irresolute couple in her usual placid manner, patiently bringing out one pair of shoes after another for the plump, and pugnaciously implacable man to try on.

After a good twenty-five minutes, the man jumped up claiming that none of the shoes were of any use to him; and without even a thank you or goodbye, he stormed off towards the door. The narrow shop was on two levels: halfway along the floor was a wide step down into the front of the shop. The man had barely reached the step when he plunged forward with such force that he landed in a heap, red faced and obviously hurt. He scrambled to his feet and glaringly looked back to see if his wife or anyone else had given him a push, but no one was anywhere near him. His wife was still buttoning her coat and making sure she had all her shopping. Miss Rolstone was busily tidying away the array of shoes, and everyone else was suitably occupied.

Heather had witnessed the whole thing and could not help but wonder if their resident ghost had been 'helping him off "her" premises'.

27

The haunting was to continue freely for the next few days.

Items would frequently go missing, but only things belonging to the shop. Of course this could be construed as carelessness, except for the fact that some duties were done so carefully. A place for everything and everything in its place was an adhered-to rule. Even Mrs Clayman could not find fault on that score.

One of the girls had gone into the staff room to attend to the weekly repairs. The entire task was performed at one side of the staff room, where an old sideboard contained everything that would be required. The work consisted of unpacking a large box of repaired shoes from the factory, taking out the repair book from the sideboard drawer in which to write all the relevant information. Then each pair of shoes would be placed in a brown paper bag with the price and customer's name written on the bag with a large, black marker pen. The pen, too, was always kept in the sideboard drawer. Never, ever, was it taken out of the staff room. There was no other such marker pen used in the shop, so everyone was puzzled when it was missing. The girls searched high and low, but the pen could not be found.

Some time later, one of the girls casually went into the lavatory, and there was the missing marker pen, standing upright in front of the toilet bowl.

The staff all took turns in cleaning the lavatory, tiny kitchen and staff room every Friday morning. Mrs Clayman, who ruled the roost with a strong will, was most particular about the cleanliness of the shop, almost to the point of obsession. No one, to her mind, could ever bring a shine to anything better than herself, so everyone became accustomed to her inspection of their work. The moment the toilet, sink, floors and staff room were finished, Mrs Clayman would give it a thorough once-over with her eagle eyes while whoever's task this had been, would hold their breath until she gave a curt nod of her head, and the morning coffee could be made and enjoyed in peace.

One particular Friday morning, Mrs Clayman entered the staff room only to come storming out in a rage a moment later. 'Fancy!' she exclaimed. 'Honestly! To leave it like that ... Supposing someone wanted to use it,' she shuddered. 'Where's Doris? Doris! Doris!' she screeched in a terrible voice as she marched through the shop searching every hiding place.

Meanwhile, the girls, hardly able to contain their curiosity, rushed into the staff room, then the tiny kitchen and finally the lavatory. At the lavatory doorway, heads crammed and muted gasps of horror escaped. Scouring powder had been sprinkled *everywhere*, by someone gone mad. Their first thought was that the scouring powder container had somehow exploded, blasting its contents throughout the entire volume of the tiny room. But this theory was refuted by the empty container found discarded but intact in a corner behind the toilet bowl.

Everyone rushed back into the shop as the unfortunate Doris returned, innocently humming a cheery tune, and carrying under her arm a packet of toilet tissues she had just been to the shops for.

'Fancy!' Mrs Clayman yelled at her. 'Leaving it like that . . . Someone may have wanted to use it!'

Doris blushed furiously. She was a cheerful middle-aged woman, who naturally did not take kindly to such venom being directed at her. She was patently mystified as she followed Mrs Clayman into the offending area.

'I didn't leave it like this!' said Doris in defence of herself, and looking as appalled as everyone else.

Mrs Clayman groaned and looked shocked. Doris, to her mind, had now committed an even greater sin, that of not admitting her disgraceful treatment of the sacred loo! Mrs Clayman was not civil to anyone for the rest of the day.

While no one dared to contradict Mrs Clayman, two of the girls could confirm that the lavatory was spotlessly clean when Doris left for the shops and nobody had been in there until Mrs Clayman started her inspection.

Having one's name called while sitting on the loo, eerie noises rising from the cellar, and the staff feeling a touch or push when no one was near; even spates of the phone ringing again and again only to stop before anyone had a chance to answer it; the occurrence of all these phenomena increased tremendously when Heather joined the staff, to the effect that hardly a day went by without some incident — especially someone rushing out of the lavatory asking who wanted them so urgently.

As one of the girls so aptly remarked: 'It is a poor do when one can't pee in peace.' She had been sitting on the loo while everyone else was in the adjoining staff room, and came rushing out only to discover all the staff chatting merrily and drinking their coffee, oblivious to the shouts that had just beckoned her.

A few months after Heather joined the staff, the shop was closed for some weeks and completely refurbished from ceiling to cellar. Even the loo was replaced. The haunting has not been known to recur from that day to this. Strangely enough, the staff, perhaps with the exception of Mrs Clayman, actually missed their resident ghost.

Uncle Gilbert

This case came to our attention two months after the event, when Missy volunteered for a survey we were conducting into psychic children. In the general questioning about paranormal involvement, she told of the following events. Her statement was confirmed by the other witnesses involved and the hardest part of this case was the long wait for the ghost to appear again, which it did, and under strictly controlled conditions.

THE LARGE, OLD house in Riverside, California, had only recently been converted into a small, homely apartment house. Little in the way of modernisation was afforded by the minimum of work performed, the house being much the same as before, except that now each floor contained separate living quarters. The old furniture left in the house from its former days as a family home, and additional furniture bought from a furniture rental company gave it a lived-in atmosphere, to which even the modicum of new bathroom and kitchen fitments looked sorely out of place.

Patrick and Laura were the first of the new occupants, taking the downstairs apartment. Their friendliness was greatly appreciated by Missy who, two weeks later, accepted Patrick's kind offer of assistance when she moved into the upstairs apartment. Missy, being a single parent with a baby of eleven months, would have otherwise found the task of carrying everything up the narrow staircase something of a struggle. The good deed helped to forge a close friendship between the three young people and thereupon developed a comradeship of the type not frequently seen these days.

Missy was keen on cooking and loved to experiment with new dishes. She often cooked a meal which the three would share in her own apartment or the one downstairs. To Laura, however, cooking was a necessity rather than a pleasure, and remained such, despite learning some new recipes from Missy. When it was Laura's turn to prepare the meal, it was plain but wholesome, and provided a healthy alternative to Missy's flamboyant style. Patrick was certainly no cook; although he gladly volunteered to wash the dishes, as well as cleaning and doing any other jobs which he could help with.

So enthusiastic was he to do his fair share of the chores, that he would be secretly hurt if either Laura or Missy as much as changed a light bulb by themselves instead of asking him.

Importantly, no one was an imposition and each had their privacy respected out of common courtesy. Borrowing became extinct by the birth of friendship gifts ranging from a desperately required carton of milk to unexpected presents of jewellery, clothes and an assortment of other personal and household requirements.

Babysitting was never a problem for Missy, as both Patrick and Laura gladly looked after little Sam. The young couple soon became experts at feeding and changing Sam, and treated him as their own son. Their flourishing relationship made it possible for Missy to consider, and secure a part-time evening job; Patrick and Laura both worked during the day and happily agreed to babysit for Sam in the evenings.

It proved an ideal arrangement, even if somewhat unusual. Patrick and Laura would leave at about eight o'clock in the morning to go to work. Missy spent some afternoons downstairs, having volunteered to do the young couple's laundry. Later, she might prepare the evening meal, providing a succulent treat for Patrick and Laura on their return home. After dinner, Patrick washed the dishes and Laura played with Sam while Missy showered, dressed and set off for work. When Missy returned home, Sam would be safely tucked up in bed with either Patrick or Laura watching over him.

Such was the awareness between the two families that Missy thought it distinctly odd when, just after lunch, she heard noises in the apartment below, as if someone was moving around. She felt sure her friends would have mentioned it if one of them was going to be at home. After the sound of doors being closed, all went quiet except for the music drifting up through the floor.

Missy put down her recipe book, picked up Sam and carried him downstairs. She knocked on the door of the downstairs apartment, but there was no answer. The music could now easily be distinguished as coming from the old radio, an outdated but quality device supplied with the apartment. Missy tentatively tried the door. It opened. Holding the door slightly ajar, she called out to Laura, then to Patrick, and was surprised to hear an unfamiliar voice answer.

'Well, hello. Come on in and sit yourself down.'

She turned to the corner of the living room from where the strange voice had spoken, and sitting in the easy chair beside the radio was an old man with white hair. His skin was heavily wrinkled and one could see the bold shape of his skull beneath the weathered flesh. She was alarmed by his presence, not knowing who he was, but his kindly face and sparkling eyes quelled her initial panic. Had he been a young man, she would surely have run screaming into the street, but this man was old and appeared to be a gentle character.

Clutching her baby tightly to her chest, Missy entered the living room, stopping in the centre where she had the benefit of a quick escape should she need it. She asked who he was and what he was doing here.

He replied that his name was Gilbert but everyone called him Gil. He went on to say: 'When my wife died, there was not much left to live for. My only family still alive is my nephew, but he's such a busy young man that we hardly ever saw each other. So I sold my home in Oregon and moved out here to be near him.'

He then asked Missy about her baby son and seemed to delight in the playful amusement of such a young mind. As the conversation continued, Missy was becoming more at ease and offered to make some lemon tea. The enjoyment on Gil's face was evident as he remarked how great it was to be spoiled.

Missy came out of the kitchen with two cups of hot lemon tea. Instantly, she wondered if it was irresponsible to leave Sam on the living room carpet, alone with the old man. But her fears soon ceased when she entered the living room to Sam's laughter as he busily pulled at Gil's shoelaces.

She placed Gil's cup on a small table close to his chair and pulled Sam to her knee, sitting on the sofa across from the old man.

Gil quickly sipped at his hot drink and remarked how he loved listening to the radio. He then started talking about various people in his family as if Missy knew every one of them intimately. Even though she tried to grasp the story he related, she soon became lost in the genealogy of Gil's family.

Missy was in considerable confusion as to whose aunt, Betty was; and whether it was Gil's aunt Mabel's or his second cousin Jennifer's son who layed claim to one of British Columbia's biggest gold strikes and then lost every cent of his vast fortune at the gambling table, and was reputed to have mysteriously disappeared while searching for his next chance of striking gold. But relief came by way of the mildly offensive smell now challenging Missy's nostrils and indicating that Sam was in need of changing. Even so, she let a good twenty minutes slip by in her bid not be rude, before she was finally forced to interrupt Gil in order to excuse herself, so she could go upstairs to her apartment to change Sam.

Gil seemed happy to continue listening to the radio, so she decided to stay in her apartment until Patrick and Laura arrived home. It would take some time to clear her mind of the saga Gil bestowed upon her and she felt exhausted just listening to him.

The knocking at the door awoke Missy from her impromptu sleep. It was Laura's turn to make dinner and Patrick had come to announce that it was almost ready.

She called out to him that she would be down in a minute. Sam had fallen asleep on his mother and she almost had to slide herself from under him to stand up. She went to the bathroom to wash the sleep from her face, and when she returned, Sam was awake. She picked him up and descended the stairs.

Patrick was telling Laura about some trouble at work, stopping briefly to greet Missy as she entered. Missy still felt tired and only now remembered with embarrassment that she did not wash the cups from her earlier chat with Gil. She knew Laura would not mind really; nevertheless, it was a courtesy she liked to observe. She wondered where Gil was, but assumed he must be outside, as the patio doors were open. Laura announced that dinner was about to be served.

Seated at the table in the dining room, Missy immediately apologised for leaving the cups in the living room earlier. Laura brushed the apology aside saying it was alright and that it had been no trouble to wash two cups.

'Where's Gil? Is he not joining us for dinner?' Missy enquired.

'Who?' asked Laura.

'Patrick's uncle, Gil. I met him this afternoon', explained Missy.

'*My* uncle? I don't have an uncle named Gil!' Patrick remarked.

Missy corrected her appellation to Uncle Gilbert; concluding that he said everyone called him Gil.

Patrick reiterated that he had neither an Uncle Gil, nor an Uncle Gilbert. He and Laura now looked uneasily at Missy.

With bewilderment, Missy gave an account of her surprising encounter that afternoon.

Patrick and Laura could offer no explanation, as neither of them knew the man Missy described. The radio was switched off when they arrived home from work and the only indication of a visitor, was given by the two empty cups in the living room. The fact that two cups had been used did not worry them in the least, as they trusted Missy implicitly.

The couple were prepared to dismiss the encounter, but they could see how distraught Missy was. She was fighting with her memory to find some clue which would confirm that it was not simply a dream. Surely if she had been dreaming, how could the two cups found in the living room be explained? They were exactly where Missy remembered them to be when she left for her own apartment to change Sam.

Patrick assured Missy that he would look into the matter tomorrow and suggested they forget about it for now, and enjoy the meal before it went cold.

The following lunchtime, Patrick, true to his word, telephoned Mr Burnhart, the owner, to enquire if anyone else had a key to the house. Mr Burnhart assured him the locks had been changed during conversion of the house. Only the three of them and himself had keys. Patrick related the strange tale of the old man, but all Mr Burnhart could offer by way of an explanation was that someone must have carelessly left the doors unlocked and some vagrant had simply walked in.

That evening, Patrick carefully repeated his conversation with Mr Burnhart, admitting how unlikely the explanation was. There was no doubt about the doors being securely locked when he and Laura left for work, *and* when they returned. Missy had not been out of the house that day so whoever the visitor was, he must have had his own key.

Three weeks later, the owner arrived to collect the monthly rent. Missy was dressing for work while Patrick and Laura looked after Sam.

Mr Burnhart asked Patrick if they had seen any more of the old man. Patrick told him they had not.

This time, the owner was more curious about the mysterious intruder, and asked for a description so that he could inform the police if the stranger returned. He did not explain that on reflection, he had considered it his responsibility to ensure the security and protection of his investment. After all, if he himself was not concerned about uninvited strangers walking into his building, why should anyone else be? Next time, there might be more cause for alarm.

Patrick shouted for Missy, who came downstairs from her apartment and repeated her account once more.

Mr Burnhart busily wrote down the details, and while reviewing them mentally, he informed them he would have a casual talk with the police about it in the morning.

Suddenly, all colour drained from his face. He looked up from his notes and fumbled for a chair into which he slumped heavily.

Laura directed Patrick to bring a glass of water for him.

Mr Burnhart drank slowly. Tears were streaming down his face as he spoke. 'It was the date that confirmed my thoughts,' he stammered, while tapping at his notes. 'I knew I recognised it. Then it all made sense. You see, this was my Uncle Gil's house, he left it to me when he died. He always used to sit in that easy chair in the corner,' his head nodding in that direction, 'listening to the radio. This description you gave me, it fits him exactly. No one looked like Uncle Gil. His head gave you the creeps, but he had the kindest eyes and face that I ever saw.'

He begged to be told eveything that the old man had said and done, how he looked — everything; to the last minute detail.

Missy re-enacted the encounter for him, trying to be as lucid as possible. She told him about the relatives she could remember Gil talking about. Mr Burnhart confirmed his knowledge of both the relatives and the few details Missy could associate with them. He was even more visibly shocked by Missy's knowledge of the gold-searching gambler in his family.

Mr Burnhart wiped the tears from his eyes and stood up. 'And there I was, calling my Uncle Gil a vagrant and having every intention of reporting him to the police.' He smiled now, as did everyone.

'I'm alright now,' he said with obvious embarrassment. He took a final gulp of the water and placed the glass down on the table.

Turning to Missy, he gripped her shoulder briefly in gratitude. 'I am sorry to embarrass you like this,' addressing them all, 'but Uncle Gil was like a father to me. We often sat in this room talking about who did what in the family, and listening to the radio. It was really because I could not bear to sell his house, that I had it converted into apartments.'

Missy expressed regret for causing his upset.

'Oh no, no,' he spurted, 'You have not upset me. On the contrary. It is a long time since I have felt so happy!' He thanked them for their sympathetic understanding and headed towards the door.

Patrick reminded him about the rent.

'What . . . Oh, forget it. I think you have all earned a free month after what you have just told me. I am very sorry though, if Gil has caused you any worry.'

He bade them goodnight, assuring them they probably would not see his uncle for some time now. Mr Burnhart had recognised the date because it was the date of the first anniversary of his uncle's death.

Missy moved out of her apartment seven months later. Patrick and Laura still live in theirs today, and Mr Burnhart has granted them a free month each year, in loving memory of Uncle Gil.

'The Smallest Haunted Cottage'

This occurrence miraculously unfolded before our very eyes. In light of this, and because it took place so naturally, the investigative team was blessed with a taste of what any percipient of a haunting may encounter: psychological disbelief and physical reality, experienced in the same instant. Our initial introduction into such a privileged position came about in the normal line of psychical research, in that while Billie was residing in the United States, she was involved in a psychic-link, dream experiment with a friend of hers in Britain. Investigators in Britain were thrilled with the result of the experiment, but the team in the United States received an unexpected bonus, which was reported to them immediately after Billie's first sighting of the ghost. The cottage in question was examined the following day and found to be quite normal. Only its occupant can be described as paranormal. This case is rare in that it represents a haunting which lends itself easily to examination in the laboratory.

THE COTTAGE IN question has remained in the same family for many years. It has been passed from one generation to another, not as any normal inheritance, but more in the way of wanting to keep such a treasure in the family and, at the same time, having an overwhelming desire to get rid of it.

Its title, 'The Smallest Haunted Cottage', was not given lightly. But it is one which is deserved.

The cottage, which has a frontage of little more than fifteen centimetres, and an approximate floor area of just 196 square centimetres, is in fact an oblong pottery container. It was made by a pottery in Hanley, Staffordshire, and decorated in the style of a country cottage with the lid serving as a thatched roof, complete with attic windows and chimney.

In 1982, Mrs Hilary Spence left the United States for a two-week vacation in England, the country of her birth. An important aspect of her itinerary were the planned visits to all the family she had not seen since she left to start a new life in the United States twelve years previously.

In the town of Bolton, Greater Manchester, during a visit with her Aunt Jean, Hilary was invited to view Jean's attic. In it she kept a collection of ornaments, pots and pans, blankets, and an assortment of other personal possessions she had not the space for elsewhere in her house. Jean told Hilary she could have whatever she could find a use for.

Hilary rummaged through the jumbled items, and finally uncovered a little pottery cottage. 'Oh, that is cute!' she said, carefully picking it up and admiring it from all angles in the dim light.

'Take it!' Jean demanded urgently. 'I am very glad you chose that, you are welcome to it.'

Hilary was both shocked and puzzled by the panic in Jean's voice, as her tone was very much out of character for such a mild mannered woman. The sharp snap of Jean's voice compelled Hilary to make absolutely sure she could indeed take the cottage. Jean assured her with certainty that she was only too glad to be rid of it, and emptied the bobbins of cotton from it with a fevered eagerness, stating she had some newspapers in which it could be wrapped for the journey to America.

All that was mentioned about the history of the cottage, was that it was given to Jean some years earlier by a family member.

Back at her single storey home in Las Vegas, Nevada, Hilary displayed her newly acquired ornament proudly on the long breakfast bar which separated the kitchen from the living area. The open-plan design gave the house a lovely airy feel and seemed to expand its size to portray the inside to be larger than the outside.

Within days, the ornamental cottage became filled with all kinds of things: wrapping tape, pens, stamps, shopping list, etcetera.

Almost immediately, Hilary started to notice a strange shadow which seemed to lurk in the vicinity of the bathroom door, just off one corner of the living room. But she was not one to be scared by such things and concluded that it was merely something bizarre which she could not explain.

The shadow continued to appear near the bathroom door and Hilary also noticed an eerie feeling each time she passed the breakfast bar, just where the cottage was situated. Occasionally, she would see the ghost of a man casually walking through the house as if he belonged there. She had seen no ghosts in her home prior to bringing the cottage back from England, and the evidence pointed overwhelmingly to the phenomena emanating from her recently acquired, family heirloom.

During the course of the following year, Hilary told no one about the strange phenomena associated with the haunted cottage, even though it was admired by all who visited.

Hilary's daughter, Billie, really took a liking to the cottage, which she mentioned each time she saw it.

On Billie's third visit following her mother's vacation in England, she was sitting talking with her mother across the breakfast bar when she suddenly shivered as if cold. It was a scorching hot summer's day with a temperature of around forty-three degrees Celsius and certainly not a day for one to feel cold, despite the old air-conditioning unit working overtime in its feeble battle against the harsh effects of the heat outside the building. But it was not exactly cold that Billie felt, it was an instinctive reaction to the materialisation of a ghostly figure standing beside her.

As if on cue, Hilary said, 'It's alright Billie, he won't harm you.' At the same time mentally noting Billie's proximity to the cottage: her hand rested less than ten centimetres away from it.

Billie was more intrigued than afraid. Nevertheless, the figure quickly transformed into a simple, vague outline with a fuzzy centre. Then, after a few seconds, it vanished.

As the weeks went by, Hilary became quite worried by her own uneasy feelings towards the cottage, and so she decided to move it to a wooden display cabinet directly opposite the end of the breakfast bar. Its glass doors offered her the comfort of containing the strange happening which was somehow caused by this unusual pottery.

One day, while Hilary was seated at the end of the breakfast bar, she heard the door slam, as if someone had just entered the house. She turned her head, but there was no one there. Ignoring it, she returned her attention to her ice-cold glass of beer on the breakfast bar. After a few minutes, she felt someone behind her. She was alone in the house, so she knew that what her senses indicated to her was impossible. Yet the hairs now bristled on the back of her neck in response to someone standing very close behind her. She spun round suddenly on her bar stool, in time to see a dense shadow fade into nothing. Her staring eyes then immediately and automatically focused directly ahead at the ornamental cottage in the display cabinet. She felt as if the cottage was staring back at her. But of course, that was ludicrous, a pot cottage cannot stare! But her thoughts strongly suggested to her that it could be something inside, which stared at her! It gave her such a fright, that she vowed never again to sit with her back to the cottage. Neither did she have any wish to sit facing it.

On Billie's next visit, she again remarked how much she adored the cottage. To her surprise, Hilary told her she could have it. 'It's not settled here,' she said ominously. 'And I know it will be alright with you.'

Billie loved to collect old pottery and was only too happy to have this old cottage join her toby jugs, ribbon plates and so forth. She asked if her mother was sure about giving it to her, feeling a little guilty for her constant reminding of her admiration for the cottage.

Hilary insisted that Billie should take it home with her, and proceeded to relate for the first time, how unusual Jean's reaction had been in giving it to her.

Billie took the cottage home and had thought to keep cookies in it; she never did, for the simple reason that every now and then when she lifted the lid a strange smell would come from inside. She decided instead to use it for pens, and other small items, the sort that one can never find when needed.

Three days later, Billie was reading a book, when a shadow fell across the page. She looked up and there in front and slightly to one side of her, was the same ghostly figure that she had seen five weeks earlier at her mother's house. He was standing so close that she automatically jerked backwards against the firmness of the sofa. A moment later he was gone.

Billie witnessed the phenomena on another four occasions at intervals of approximately two weeks.

Busily typing one evening, she was suddenly aware of someone behind her. She looked round in time to see just a dark shadow before it melted into the air.

Throughout those few months, Billie soon realised the connection between the ghostly figure and the cottage. This she confirmed with her mother on her next visit.

While Billie was calmly intrigued by the haunted cottage, it was still a shock to have either a shadow or a distinct figure making these sudden appearances. Her apartment, a short walk from the frequently-filmed bright lights of Downtown Las Vegas, was a little too small for an additional occupant, ghostly or not.

After a considerable amount of experimentation by trying different items inside the cottage, the effect was, if anything, an increase in the sightings. She finally decided that the cottage should be left empty and not handled, so she took everything out and made sure its lid was firmly in place.

Surprisingly, this simple exercise seems to have trapped the occurrence inside the cottage, from which it cannot escape, or does not wish to.

Unlike her mother, Billie had retained her British nationality while living in the United States. When she moved back to England, the haunted cottage and its strange contents returned with her. It now stands beside other old ornaments, with the lid tightly in place, and locked in a display case.

If it had not been for Billie's return to England in 1983, America could have gained yet another of Britain's national treasures. This British ghost has an enviable track record of flying twelve thousand miles by plane, as well as having 'resided' in a foreign country for a year and a half. Complete with a Certificate of Authenticity, 'The

Smallest Haunted Cottage', which proved to be one of the easiest cases to confirm, has attracted offers as high as 12,000 US dollars, all of which have been politely refused.

Taxi For Irene

When Gary telephoned me one Monday morning to report his first sighting of a ghost two days earlier, he was more unbelieving of the ghost than I was. He seemed surprised that I would take such a bizarre event so seriously, but unknown to him, he had mentioned several esoteric points which made his statement weigh heavily on the side of the truth. What no one knew at that time, was that the investigation was to reveal another, less charming aspect to the haunting, which was to split the case into two separate ones. The case of Irene was addressed less than a week after the report was made, while the second case, involving a ghost by the name of Patsy Hardy, has been the subject of a continuous and extremely exhaustive research programme for the previous two years, which is long after the hauntings had ceased. An interesting aspect in the details to follow is that the first sighting was of Patsy, while the second was of Irene. The case illustrates perfectly the natural ease with which two entities can be mistakenly construed as one, without any fault whatsoever on the part of the witnesses.

B Y TRADITION, THE media are indelibly remembered for two main attitudes towards the paranormal: one, that they have an incredible ability to create sensation, by twisting facts or taking quotes totally out of context; and two, that they are unmovable sceptics, who seem to continually, even if unintentionally, cause ridicule to befall a percipient of a paranormal experience.

It is little wonder then, that when a report of a haunting is received from the media itself, the credibility of the report seems to automatically become questionable. Nevertheless, sceptics throughout the world provide almost as many reported hauntings as do believers; and to be honest, even the sceptical media are not immune to an occasional ghost or two. Some may enhance the sensationalism of a haunting, while others, as in this case, had a ghost thrust upon them unexpectedly and quite alarmingly.

Gary, a normally sceptical reporter for Radio City in Liverpool, Merseyside, had just come downstairs from the newsroom when his attention was drawn to a heavy, lead-filled door which opened and then closed apparently by itself. He was not sure he could believe his eyes as he noticed just the leg of a woman disappear round the closing soundproof door. He then heard footsteps running along the corridor beyond, towards Studio 3. Gary found this also very odd, as the radio station, out of a necessity for quality broadcasts, was thickly carpeted to completely absorb any sounds of footsteps.

It was twenty minutes to two on Saturday morning, so Gary immediately checked with the security guard, who was in the front reception area, to determine who was wandering around inside the building at such a late hour. The guard told him that apart from the two of them, there was John Jessop, and DJ John Storey, who was on the air broadcasting the *Downtown* programme.

Both Gary and the security guard started a methodical search of the entire building, which only verified there was no intruder. They checked with John Storey to see if he had been out of his studio at all, but he had not seen anyone.

Without being able to find an acceptable explanation for what Gary witnessed, they went back to the reception area where they were greeted by a taxi driver knocking on the all-glass door at the entrance.

Momentarily forgetting their dilemma, they became curious to discover what the taxi driver could possibly want at that time in the morning.

The guard opened the door which, being a security door, was electronically locked. The taxi driver told them he had a taxi outside for Irene. Gary and the guard looked at each other with puzzled expressions and explained to the driver that there was no one in the building by that name, in fact, neither of them knew anyone called Irene.

The driver told them his company had received a phone call from a woman who said her name was Irene, asking for a taxi to pick her up outside Radio City's entrance.

Again, they informed him nobody of that name worked at Radio City. Indeed currently there were no women at all in the radio station.

The driver argued that he had just seen a young blonde girl walk into the building as he pulled up; she had apparently waved to him as if to say she would be out in a moment.

Gary and the guard looked more puzzled. They explained that no one could possibly have entered the building, as the door could only be unlocked by the security guard. And, as the driver would have seen, the two of them had only just returned to reception; before that, it had been empty.

Impatiently, the driver insisted that the girl had walked up to the door and gone inside.

They reiterated emphatically that the door was electronically controlled and there was absolutely no means by which anyone could simply walk in off the street without the security guard first letting them in.

Forced to accept their explanation, the taxi driver stormed off, not knowing he had been the second person that night to have witnessed a ghostly presence at Radio City.

This was to be the start of a series of strange, overnight phenomena attributed to Irene as she was thereafter referred to.

Realising they had an extremely interesting story, Radio City recorded on tape later that night, their news bulletin of ghostly Irene, for broadcast the following day. But when they played the tape the next day, they were shocked to find it was completely blank. The tape had been carefully labelled and there was no doubt it was the correct tape. They considered whether someone had accidentally erased the bulletin, but had to discount that idea as there was no trace of background noise associated with the tape having been erased. It was totally and utterly blank, as if the story had never been taped. All the other tapes in the same rack were alright and they had to quickly record once more the story of Irene for their news broadcast.

If the news was not safe from this ghostly interloper, neither was newscaster Tony Kerner two weeks later, who, after reading the four o'clock news bulletin on Friday morning, went upstairs to find all his cigarettes scattered all over the desk. He noticed one of them had been lit and, in disbelief, he watched it smoulder in the ashtray.

He returned downstairs, determined to find out if someone had been playing a practical joke on him. The only people other than himself in the building, were John Storey in the studio, and Stephen on security, and they were not able to offer any explanation, as neither of them had been in the newsroom.

They were all discussing the bizarre event when suddenly, the telephone in reception began to ring. They were surprised at this, not because it was ten-past-four in the morning, but because the phone in reception cannot *ring* at night unless someone dials from within the building; and the only three people still working at that hour, were all together listening to the phone ring. After all that had happened, who could be blamed for not answering it?

Early Morning Ghost Call

When one comes across cases such as this, it almost suggests there is a conspiracy to keep hauntings a secret. In some respects, this is true. Few individuals have a desire to have hordes of strangers marching through their home in an attempt to see the ghost. A hotel is no different in that it relies on its guests returning because of the excellent service it provides, not because they were disturbed in the middle of the night by a ghost. Mr Fourche did not believe in ghosts, but he telephoned us immediately after his vacation in the hope of verifying that the hotel was not simply 'passing the buck'. The hotel was helpful in allowing us access to the particulars of past residents, and we were able to inform Mr Fourche later, that while he was not alone in his doubt about the presence of a ghost, the evidence for a haunting was unshakeable.

A S A PRETTY fourteen-year-old schoolgirl, it would be untrue to say Sonya Fourche had no imagination, indeed it would be unnatural if she did not. However, there is a definite distinction between imagination and reality, irrespective of how bizarre the reality may be.

Certainly, Sonya wondered if her mind might have been playing tricks on her during a cool August weekend while staying at a small, family-run hotel in southern Alberta, but in all honesty, she knew what she witnessed was no deception of the mind.

Sonya and her parents had spent the previous week with relatives in Prince Albert, Saskatchewan, and were staying at the hotel for just two nights while they toured Jasper and Banff National Parks, and visited Medicine Hat and Cypress Hills Provincial Park, before continuing to Vancouver for the remaining four days of their two-week vacation.

Like most teenagers, Sonya was not known for being an early riser. It usually took a great amount of effort from her mother to get her out of bed in the mornings. As a diabetic, it was essential for Sonya to be woken at eight every morning to give herself an injection of insulin, a necessity which could not be waived for any reason. Therefore it was arranged that Sonya should receive an early morning alarm call at precisely eight o'clock on the two mornings the family would remain at the hotel. It was also made known that she would require a breakfast, which was to be left outside her door as a further incentive for her to get out of bed.

Surprisingly, the hotel was not busy, despite its auspicious location, with the Canadian Rockies to the west and the Great Plains to the east. Sonya was given room number six and her parents were offered room eight, at the end of a small corridor. The rooms were comfortable, immaculate, and of a reasonable size. The hotel was not new, but the homeliness of it was hardly congenial for conjuring up images of ghosts, past or present.

They were informed on their arrival, that dinner would not be ready for another hour, so the family went upstairs to unpack and discuss their itinerary for the weekend, as well as their subsequent route to Vancouver, British Columbia. They decided to make for Fort Macleod, then follow Provincial Highway 3 to Vancouver, stopping overnight, possibly at Trail, British Columbia.

After dinner on Friday evening, the family took a leisurely drive through the surrounding area, as they planned to see as much as they could during their short stay in Alberta.

Arriving back at the hotel shortly before ten o'clock, an early night was decided, as they had a busy schedule on Saturday. Besides, the fresh air alone would be likely to have an effect on Sonya, and there was a possibility she would sleep right through her alarm call, without the addition of late nights. Mr Fourche mentioned this to the desk clerk before he retired for the night, and was assured they would let Sonya's phone ring until she answered.

The following morning, the phone in Sonya's room suddenly burst into life. Finally, Sonya reluctantly dragged herself out of bed and lifted the receiver. A pleasant, efficient female voice said: 'Good morning! This is your eight a.m. wake-up call. Your breakfast will be outside your door in five minutes.'

It was a cold morning. Pulling aside the heavy, red velvet drapes, Sonya grimaced at the sight of a grey sky and lashing rain. Quickly she pulled on her warm dressing gown, gave herself an injection of insulin and, there as promised, outside her door was the source of the tantalising aroma which permeated her room: the welcomed breakfast and hot, freshly made coffee.

The next morning, Sonya once more groped sleepily for the ringing phone. Again a pleasant voice informed her that this was her eight a.m. wake-up call, and breakfast would be outside her door in five minutes. The bed was warm and cosy, and Sonya could hardly keep her eyes open. But she managed to stumble out of bed, switch on the light and snuggle into her gown. Her injection over with,

Sonya opened her door. She blinked and stared at the vacant carpet. No coffee, nor breakfast. Sonya shrugged, closed the door and decided she may as well take a quick shower.

About fifteen minutes later, now fully awake and wearing warm jeans and a sweater, Sonya opened the door again, hoping the breakfast would not be stone cold. But there was still no evidence of it, not even the rich aroma she had delighted in the previous morning. Feeling irritable, Sonya glanced down the corridor wondering if it had been left outside one of the other rooms. No. Nothing. No sight nor sound of anything.

She hurried to her parents' room, thinking that it was strange they were not about yet. Entering their room, she found them both sound asleep.

Sonya laughed at the sight and shouted: 'Come on you guys, it's time to get up!' as she playfully bounced up and down on their bed.

Her mother stirred and gazed sleepily at her daughter, asking what time it was. Sonya told her it must be at least eight-thirty by now.

Mrs Fourche grappled for her travel alarm clock and squinted at it. 'Oh, Sonya, it's barely five in the morning!'

'Can't be,' Sonya squealed, thinking of those lost lovely hours of sleep she might have had. 'I got my eight o'clock alarm call. And they never brought me any breakfast.'

'Someone's been playing a joke on you!' Mrs Fourche said angrily. 'Just wait until I see the desk clerk . . . Go back to your room, honey.'

Back in her room, Sonya checked her own watch, it read 5.13 a.m. She was more upset than angry. What sort of person would do such a thing? She had taken her insulin three hours before she need have done. It should not have any adverse effect, but it was not something to play around with, and she was desperate for something to eat.

A little after eight o'clock, the family confronted the woman who was attending the reception desk. She was a smart lady in her early thirties, and gave an air of friendly efficiency. 'Good morning,' she said brightly. 'Anything I can do for you?'

'Yes! There is,' said Mrs Fourche, instantly blushing. She did not like to have to get angry with people. 'My daughter is supposed to get an eight o'clock alarm call . . .'

'Ah, yes,' the young woman quickly interrupted. 'We are running a little late this morning, I was about to make the call now, but as you are . . .'

Mrs Fourche waved this aside. 'She did get a call! At five this morning! This is no joke. My daughter . . .'

'Please, Mrs Fourche,' the young woman looked appalled, 'there must be some mistake?'

'Sonya.' Mrs Fourche pushed her daughter forward. 'Tell her what happened!'

Sonya explained that the call had been exactly the same as the one she had received the previous morning, word for word. The only difference being that there was no breakfast left outside her door. Then she explained about waking her mother, there was no doubt that it was around five a.m.

'I want to see whoever was on this desk last night', said Mr Fourche, feeling he ought to contribute some of his authority. 'I think at least an apology is required.' The young woman shook her head, stultified.

'Excuse me, but there is no one on the desk until eight o'clock, Mr Fourche. In fact, the telephones are switched off all night so that none of the guests are disturbed by the phones ringing. So I can't think how this has happened.' Then suddenly her eyes widened. 'Oh! Wait a minute. Your daughter is in room number six, right?'

Sonya nodded her head, but protested that she did not see what her room number had to do with anything.

The young woman held up her hands and smiled. 'Excuse me, please.' She bent down to search among the drawers of the desk, and a few seconds later pulled out a black, hard bound book. 'There!' She triumphantly slapped it down on the top of the desk. 'Might I offer a sincere apology. This has happened before you see, but only ever in room number six. We had a desk clerk who died in the hotel some years ago, and I am afraid she still seems to take her duties seriously every now and then. I wonder, if I could trouble you to write your experience in this book. As you can see, many others have done so over the years.' Sonya gulped.

'You mean to say my alarm call this morning was made by a . . . a . . . *ghost?*'

'Yes Miss,' the young woman said earnestly with a friendly, honest, Canadian smile lighting up her face, 'Quite definitely, yes!'

Prelude To Tragedy

For a natural phenomenon, chance has caused many bizarre situations. And possibly this case is so unusual because chance has also intervened here. It is indeed a rarity as far as similar hauntings are concerned. This tragic tale came to The Institute for Psychical Research via a neighbour telling a work associate who told a friend who told a friend, who then told her friend who was a member of our organisation. The case required an extremely careful investigation because two years had since passed and there was only one eyewitness to the phenomena reported.

MARY FIRMIN MOVED into her pretty, terraced cottage in a small Yorkshire village as a bride in 1939. Her husband, Kevin, kept the narrow strip of back garden in an immaculate condition, and it was a riot of colour from March onwards.

Mary and Kevin had been married for sixteen years when, after several months of severe suffering, Kevin died from a cancer of the throat. Mary had taken on the horrendous task of nursing him at home, but she had done so willingly, despite becoming a virtual recluse and a worn-out shadow of her former self in the process.

It was Christmas Eve when Kevin died, just after three o'clock in the afternoon. Kevin's illness had been terminal; all the same, it was heart-breaking to watch him die. The moment the family doctor arrived, which was a mere formality as there was nothing anyone could do, Mary quietly slipped from the room.

She stood outside in the back garden, her arms folded about her plump body in a gesture of self-protection, dressed in a serviceable, mink-coloured woollen dress, and a floral pinafore apron, quite oblivious to the biting, ice-cold wind. Her mind was numb, and sudden lethargy acting like a drug, made her limbs and body seem too heavy to support. Mary was a widow now, with a fourteen-year-old son to raise on her own. And she doubted her ability to cope, to face the rest of her life without her beloved Kevin.

Ever since then, Mary dreaded Christmas Eve. Friends and family had over the years, repeatedly asked Mary to spend that day with them, but she always refused, feeling perhaps that it was a kind of duty to remain quietly in her cottage, thinking over the years she had shared with Kevin.

But one year, with Christmas Eve just two weeks away, Mary at last decided to break with this self-imposed tradition, and spend the day with her sister, Joan, who lived in the same village as herself. She would walk over to Joan's house that morning and talk to her about it, before her new resolve weakened.

It had been thirteen years since Kevin died. Their son Michael was now twenty-seven years old, was happily married, and had six-year-old twins, Eric and Susan. As usual, Mary looked forward to spending Christmas Day and Boxing Day at Michael's spacious bungalow, enjoying the comfort of central heating and a delicious variety of food, and most of all, the lively company of the twins.

But first, she had to get the dreaded Christmas Eve over and done with.

Joan was both surprised and delighted by Mary's request. She thought it was about time Mary stopped hiding herself away every Christmas Eve. She was a widow herself, and like her sister, she too had brought up a son on her own for many years.

Joan's son, Gordon, who at the age of thirty-one, seemed a confirmed bachelor, came home for his lunch that day, and on hearing of his aunt's plan to spend Christmas Eve at their home, offered to pick her up in his van. It was only a ten-minute walk, but was such a kind gesture that Mary politely accepted.

After lunch, Joan said she would walk Mary back to her cottage, and then go on to the village shops.

It was bitterly cold outside. The sky, a dome of white, made the country landscape stark and bleak. The narrow pavement was slippery underfoot from a recent snowfall and the two sisters had to tread carefully as they walked arm in arm, stopping briefly now and then to chat to various acquaintances as they passed.

As they came to a bend in the road, Mary suddenly experienced the sensation of a loud buzzing sound in her ears. Normally of robust health, she could not imagine what could be causing this. But after a minute or two, it passed.

Across the narrow road lay the village church, where Kevin was buried. It looked surrealistic, like a black and white sketch. Mary found herself staring at it. Then, her gaze was brought sharply to the stone wall which surrounded the church. Time seemed to stand still. Mary could not suppress the involuntary gasp, and automatically gripped her sister's arm more tightly.

Joan was alarmed. 'Mary! Whatever is wrong?'

But Mary could only shake her head.

There was a cosy little cafe close by. Joan took the initiative and quickly ushered Mary into the warm, fragrant shop. While she was at the counter ordering their coffee, Mary rubbed condensation from the window and gazed out. She could still see the church and its stone wall from here; though thankfully, not the apparition she had seen a couple of minutes before.

It was something Mary would never forget. It was ironic; so often over the years she had wished to see her dead husband, or at least feel his presence — but she never had. And now, like a lightning bolt out of the blue, she had seen him, had seen Kevin; though she now wished desperately that she had not, it had given her such a shock.

She closed her eyes and let the image come back to her. It was not difficult. One minute she was staring at the old church, and the next thing she knew, her gaze had been brought incisively to the stone wall, like a pin attracted to a magnet.

And there he was! Her Kevin, with his wavy brown hair and pleasant, good-natured face, wearing a pair of old trousers he was fond of and a fawn polo neck sweater she had knitted for him. He looked so real, that she had gasped. He waved to her and smiled, then jerked his thumb to bring her attention to who was sitting beside him, for to Mary it seemed as if she possessed only tunnel vision. With conscious effort she had focused on the man beside Kevin and actually felt her face drain of colour. It was Gordon, Joan's son! He too had smiled and waved.

Now, as Joan came to the table with coffee and toasted, buttered currant buns, Mary felt that she must have had a brainstorm back there. She had imagined it all, surely. Yes, she must have done. After all, she had seen Gordon that morning at Joan's house — alive and well. He had been his usual, quiet, unpretentious self.

Joan was still looking anxious. Some explanation was obviously necessary, so Mary said she had experienced a bit of a sharp pain in her chest but felt well enough now.

Mary slept badly that night, and it took considerable effort as the days slowly passed by, to stop thinking about that strange occurrence.

Christmas Eve arrived. Mary packed a case, ready for going to Michael's house on Christmas Day. Just before lunch, Gordon arrived in his Escort van as promised. She was grateful for the lift to her sister's house, as she was loaded up with the case and plastic bags filled with gifts. Gordon really was a thoughtful man, she reflected; he would make a good husband and father.

That evening, the wind howled and snow began to fall thick and fast. It was cosy, sitting beside the coal fire in Joan's lounge, watching the Christmas tree and surrounding gaily-coloured gifts twinkle and dance in the firelight. The two sisters sat side by side on the couch sharing a large bowl of nuts, which Mary cracked open; her hands were not crooked with arthritis like Joan's. They were content to sit and gossip, with the radio on low, the music relaxing.

Gordon was out with friends this evening, though neither would have minded if he had stayed in; he was so unobtrusive, it was easy to forget he was in the same room.

Later, Joan suggested they go out to the White Hart for the last hour. Mary would have preferred to stay inside, but she knew her sister would not go without her, and, as Joan had formed a habit of going out to the pub for the last hour on Christmas Eve, usually with her neighbour, to enjoy a sherry and a bit of lively company, it would have appeared unsociable for Mary to refuse.

The White Hart was not far away, for which both were thankful. Even muffled up and wearing fur-lined boots, they were stiff with cold by the time they got there and the brightly-lit pub seemed overpoweringly hot for the first few minutes.

The smell of beer, spirits and cigars permeated the close atmosphere. The general hubbub made conversation difficult. Understandably, the pub was packed. Mary and Joan were lucky to have got a seat, their arrival coinciding with a couple who had just got up to leave.

Sipping their sherries, Joan remarked: 'Our Gordon should be in here somewhere with his friends, I am sure I saw his van outside.'

Mary laughed, 'We will be lucky to spot him in this crush.' She had already been knocked, nudged and bumped as people squeezed passed their table. It was no wonder neither of them noticed a flurry of activity at the other end of the room; nor a pale, shaken man trying to make himself heard as he screeched at one of the bar staff. His task finally accomplished, he jostled his way over to their end of the room. He did not notice the two sisters, he was frantically trying to get the attention of two young women a few tables away.

Only as he inadvertently knocked Joan's arm, did the two sisters break into simultaneous smiles of recognition. Joan grabbed his arm: 'Hello, Terry! Is our Gordon with you?'

The young man stared at her. His mouth dropped open and a bead of sweat trickled down his forehead. His skin was ashen, he looked bereft and uncertain. He swallowed with difficulty. 'Oh! Mrs Alcaster . . . Can you come outside.' His quest to reach the two girls was forgotten.

Joan knew something was wrong, that much was blatantly obvious. She looked at Mary with apprehension. Mary did not hesitate to follow her sister, having to push and shove to reach the door. Both had left their coats on the backs of their chairs, but the icy blast of wind that met them was soon forgotten.

A full, silvery moon illuminated the scene. A short distance away from the door of the pub, sitting leaning against the brick wall of the building, with his head slumped forward on his chest, was Gordon.

For what seemed an everlasting moment, the three of them stood rigid, rooted to the spot, with snow swirling around them, stars sparkling in the frosty sky, and the wind flapping at their clothes.

Terry had begun to shake as if convulsed. 'We came here a couple of hours ago with Sharon and Ellen,' he said in a strained voice. 'Gordon said he didn't feel so good . . . I came out with him — he looked ghastly . . . Got one of the staff to call an ambulance . . . Not much to drink . . .'

Mary managed to nod her head. She had never known Gordon to over-indulge, not even on Christmas Eve. She felt dizzy. Like Terry, she was inexplicably afraid to go near Gordon who looked as if he was unconscious.

Mary watched with sickening apprehension as Joan went over to her son. The golden light spilling from the pub windows made the snow sparkle and aided the moonlight to illuminate the still figure of Gordon. He looked strange, incongruous, sitting there on the snow covered path, his back against the pub wall, his head supported by his chest.

Mary now heard the siren of the approaching ambulance, its eerie wailing cutting through the silence.

Joan had knelt beside her son. She said his name softly and gently lifted his head.

One look was enough. Her hands dropped away as if burnt. For a horrible moment there was a heavy, silent, stillness, when all three held their breath, and stared at the still figure in a horrified fascination.

Then Joan screamed. A scream that seemed to freeze Mary's blood. The agony of it was beyond human endurance.

Joan gasped painfully to get air into her lungs: 'Gordon!' she cried; there was disbelief, fear, even anger in that one utterance. 'My boy . . . My Gordon . . . He's dead. He's dead.' Sounding like a chant now.

The ambulance was pulling into the car park.

Terry stood immobile, like one turned to stone. Mary too paid no heed to the arrival of the ambulance. Somehow she made it to the bushes growing alongside the pub. And there she vomited. As her stomach disgorged its undigested contents, her whole body revolted in disbelief of the unshakeable reality — one minute hot, the next cold. A severe buzzing started in her ears, and black spots swam before her eyes as she fought to remain conscious. It was going to be a long, everlasting, horrible night; and Joan would need her.

Deep within her turbulent mind, Mary felt an even greater affinity with her sister now Joan too had reason to dread Christmas Eve. One day she would tell Joan about seeing Gordon with Kevin — on the church wall. It might help. But right now, it was a nightmare. A ghastly incomprehensible nightmare!

Samlesbury's White Lady

The reason for many of the reports of this occurrence is even more unusual than the occurrence itself; they were made solely because no one else would believe the experience. These percipients lived with a terrible nightmare until they came to us; most have received immense relief from the knowledge that they are not alone in witnessing this bizarre manifestation. Unfortunately, some of the more sceptical ones now have a different nightmare, that of consoling themselves to the fact that they really did encounter a ghost. The case here is representative of most reports received over the past twenty years, but similar experiences have also occurred during the day. I have taken an exceptional liberty in such a factual book as this, by also including the associated legend, but I feel it is warranted for explanatory purposes, and at least the ghost exists. Nevertheless, it should be remembered that the legend, famous though it is, bears no influence whatsoever on the numerous cases on file, and neither I nor IPR lay any claim to the legend's accuracy or inaccuracy.

LANCASHIRE'S MOST FAMOUS haunting goes way back to Tudor times; yet today, some four hundred years later, the White Lady of Samlesbury still can be seen, usually by the unwary and unsuspecting traveller who knows nothing of the history surrounding Samlesbury Hall.

According to the legend, it was towards the end of the sixteenth century, at a time when the country was split apart by differing religious beliefs, that Lady Dorothy fell in love with a youthful member of a neighbouring Protestant family. The Southworths of Samlesbury Hall were staunch Roman Catholics, and could not approve of Dorothy's suitor, forbidding them to see each other. Needless to say, the romance continued albeit in secret, the young couple being forced into meeting late at night in the grounds of the hall.

The pressure on the couple soon became intolerable, and on one dark night, they decided to elope. But their plans were overheard by Lady Dorothy's brother who was hiding in the bushes nearby, listening to their conversation.

When the young groom-to-be returned to collect his intended, bringing an accomplice with him, Lady Dorothy was alarmed to see her brothers emerging from the bushes wielding swords. They ran the youth and his accomplice through without delay and their bodies were secretly buried in the grounds of the hall.

Heart-broken, Lady Dorothy is said to have wasted away until she finally died of sorrow.

Since that time, her ghost has returned to Samlesbury Hall and has been seen on a number of occasions, in the garden and grounds as well as inside the hall.

Whether the legend is true or not is difficult to ascertain, and it is beyond the scope of this book to cast judgement; apart from a mention that there are several variations of the story currently in print. As with most legendary hauntings, the details change depending on the source, although the skeletons of two young men are believed to have been found near the hall early last century.

The existence of a White Lady, however, is easier to establish than the legend surrounding her, and is confirmed by numerous and more recent reports of her appearance.

The hall is open to the public, hence several reports mention sightings of the ghost inside the hall, also the sound of her rustling skirt, and often the sound of her sobbing. In the grounds too, she has been seen frequently, walking among the trees.

More dramatically, she has given drivers on the A677, a shock of the worst severity, as she did Alex Dunderdale and his wife, on the night of November 16th, 1987.

At about eleven-thirty, the couple were returning from a visit to friends in Blackpool. Leaving the M6 motorway at junction 31, near Preston, they continued eastwards on the A677 towards their home in Blackburn. Neither had a belief in the paranormal and thought nothing of their impending closeness to Samlesbury Hall.

Within a short distance of its entrance, Alex saw a woman dash into the road in front of his car. He stamped on the brakes, knowing full well he had little chance of avoiding her. She had appeared too suddenly, too close. He felt the bump as the car hit her, followed by more bumps as the wheels ran over her limp body.

Finally, the car skidded to a halt and for what seemed an eternity, Alex sat gripping the steering wheel, not daring to get out. The sound of his wife's voice brought him out of his stupor, asking what on earth they had run over. She was not watching the road so had not seen the woman, but had certainly felt the car bounce over something which banged its way along the underside, until discharged at the rear.

Alex could not believe this was happening to him, that he had knocked down and probably killed someone. The consequences of what he had done, blameless or not, were evident in his explanation to his wife of what the car had just driven over.

Quickly and with brave determination, he opened the car door and got out. He first looked underneath, in case she was still there, caught on the exhaust pipe, perhaps. He walked all round the car, but there was no sign of the body.

Now shaking from the intense shock of his ordeal, he moved the car to the side of the road where it would not cause a further accident.

Gathering all his strength, he set out to look for the woman's body, praying he would find her dazed but unhurt, yet unable to believe she was anything but dead.

Alex walked back along the road, but could find no trace of her. He recalled she had been wearing what he took to be a long white coat and naturally assumed he would have no difficulty in finding her. He looked on both sides of the road in case she had managed to crawl across; but as his car became more and more distant, he realised the search was futile. For over half an hour he searched, only to return to his car knowing he had hit and run over a woman, yet could find no body to confirm it.

Both Alex and his wife are as sceptical now as they were before that frightful night, a night they are not likely to forget. They prefer to call it an unexplained event, a one-off for which there is no comprehensible explanation.

That might be true if this was the only case on file, but it most certainly is not. Actually, it is one of the most frequently reported aspects of this haunting, which is made public herein for the first time. In fact, there are over forty similar reports on file, in which a driver, either alone or with between one and five people, has been in collision with the White Lady of Samlesbury. All have searched for her battered body, sometimes in the pouring rain, before finally admitting defeat.

One young man was so unnerved by his experience, that he refused to return to his car; leaving it there all night, unlocked and with the window open.

In addition, many more reports include drivers catching a glimpse of the White Lady in their headlights, standing at the side of the road as if waiting for a bus. Some drivers have even stopped to pick her up, only to find that she had disappeared.

Occasionally, an unsuspecting individual walking home after missing the last bus, comes across the young woman on this lonely, eerie stretch of road; and almost has a heart attack when she appears or disappears in front of them. With little sanctuary offered on this road, these percipients often flee the rest of the way home.

The White Lady of Samlesbury Hall is one of few apparitions to be seen by more men than women, and by more sceptics than believers. And she is likely to be seen by many more yet, as she makes her ghostly trips to what was once part of the old estate's garden, which lies across the road from Samlesbury Hall.

In The Looking Glass

The mother-in-law of the percipient wrote to us some five weeks after the event, and because of the confirmation included in her initial report, it was essential to establish the exact chronological order of the events. The reporter was fearful, not of the disturbance itself, but of the possibility that her daughter-in-law might suffer a traumatic experience because of the alleged known properties of the phenomena. The percipient herself was at first hostile to an investigation being conducted because her fear of being declared insane and subsequently ridiculed, took precedence over her fear of the phenomena. Unfortunately, no amount of assurances from ourselves and her family could dispel the fear and although she finally succumbed to the eventuality of an investigation, she was understandably less than helpful. But the percipient took only a small part in the events, therefore, as soon as her statement was given, we were able to fulfil the real purpose of our visit, to investigate the phenomena.

ON THE DEATH of his grandmother, Tim Corvina and his wife Judy, came into a rather peculiar inheritance at a time when they had been married for a little over a year.

They were not well off, after paying the mortgage on their house, and almost 50 dollars a week being spent on Tim's travel costs to work in Philadelphia, Pennsylvania. The young couple knew it would not be easy those first few years, but despite Tim's parents needing to contribute 5,000 dollars towards the down payment on their house, and pay all the closing costs, Tim's second job working most evenings and every weekend ensured that they had about 100 dollars a week for the basic necessities. Providing Tim's Mustang remained reliable and there were no other unexpected expenses, they were reasonably assured of realising a significant increase in their real-estate investment in two or three years' time.

But for now, only the main rooms of their house had been furnished, leaving two bedrooms and the dining room practically empty. Tim's grandmother's old wardrobe therefore, was a welcomed addition, along with a dining table and chairs. Other furniture had been offered to them, but they could have filled their house twice over if they had accepted everything, and they had to be careful to allow for the remodelling of their home.

The wardrobe was huge, standing 215 centimetres high and about 180 centimetres wide, and there was considerable debate about how to get it through the doorways. Amid talks of having to break it up, Tim's uncle discovered that it could be taken apart as the ingenious design allowed its separation into five pieces. Hence, it was transported to Tim's house with relative ease.

The heavy wood and expert carpentry so fascinated everyone that there emerged a few family members who expressed their willingness to take it off Tim's hands any time he wished. Into this conversation came a discussion about its origin. No one was sure exactly, but most agreed in principle to the suggestion that it was a wedding present to the grandmother, which dated the wardrobe at about seventy years old. Whether it was new or not at the time was also not known. To add to the debate, a friend who was helping said he thought it was early 19th century, or even older.

Safely installed in the second bedroom of Tim's house, no one could have imagined that it was later to become the topic of much deeper discussion among the family.

The second bedroom was left undisturbed until five months later, when Judy's baby arrived earlier than expected and before conversion of the smallest bedroom to a nursery had been completed. Therefore, the young couple put the baby's crib in the second bedroom until the work was finished.

The baby seemed oblivious to the strange wardrobe, but Judy began to notice some bizarre events.

The first incident happened when Judy went to lift her son out of his crib at six o'clock one morning. He had woken crying and as hungry as ever. As Judy picked him up, she caught in the corner of her eye, a glimmer coming from the wardrobe. At first, she thought it was a reflection of light in the mirrored door and turned to the wardrobe to check its brightness, in case it could disturb the baby by shining into his crib. But it was the strangest reflection she had ever seen, more like a shimmering across the whole surface of the mirror, with different colours and intensities of light swirling around in the dull, misty glass.

She remembered cleaning the mirror only the week before, so there should not have been any dust on it.

Looking around the room for the cause of this unusual reflection, she could find nothing that would account for it. The wardrobe was in the shade of any light coming through the window, and although the baby's toys in his crib were indeed colourful, they were incapable of emitting any light.

58

Her son Michael was now clawing at her mouth, reminding her that he was hungry, so she put the oddity out of her mind and carried him downstairs.

It was later that afternoon when she next thought of her strange experience. Tim had gone to work shortly after she brought Michael downstairs, and household chores and the baby had kept her busy. She was now sitting on the settee drinking a well-earned cup of coffee; Michael was asleep on the rug and it seemed an ideal chance to check further for the source of such a peculiar reflection.

Tentatively, she entered the bedroom and, after looking around the room, walked straight to the mirrored door of the wardrobe. As she gazed into the glass, all she could see was her own reflection.

For some minutes she stood there, but not one flicker of colour appeared. She examined the mirror closely. There were some specks of dust on it, otherwise it was quite clear and not at all cloudy, as it had been earlier. Perhaps she had imagined it, she thought, and returned downstairs intending to forget all about it.

The next morning, she was about to lift Michael from his crib, when the memory of the previous day's event came flooding back. She looked immediately to the wardrobe, but again, there was no reflection except her own.

The weeks passed by without further incident. The nursery was completed and Michael and his toys moved in. The second bedroom was now left undisturbed again except for a customary weekly clean. And it was late in the morning on one such occasion that Judy entered the room.

Having forgotten about her earlier experience, she had just finished vacuuming the draperies, and turned to switch off the vacuum cleaner, when she was shocked to notice the mirror shimmering faintly. She had not yet opened the drapes again, so this time she could discount completely any reflection coming through the window. The glow from the wardrobe seemed brighter in the dull light of the room and gave the appearance of light coming from deep inside the mirror rather than being cast upon it.

Almost trance-like, she walked towards the iridescence, stopping directly in front of the mirror. As she watched in amazement, the shimmering became brighter. Her own image became faint and partial as the swirling colours gradually engulfed her reflection.

Then, she could see another image emerging through the maze of multi-coloured light. It gradually became clearer until she could distinguish that it was the image of an old woman. It appeared that she wore a white hat of some kind atop pale yellow hair. A kindly face with work-worn eyes, set in a distant gaze, gave the appearance that she was a holographic portrait trapped inside the glass mirror. Her shoulders faded into the sea of colour, but Judy could see a dark material covering them like a high-necked dress.

The old woman's image was so bright and colourful that it seemed to be stained into the glass. Yet, by comparison, Judy's own image was now but a faint outline, which she had to strain her eyes to detect.

As she looked back to the woman's face, the eyes had now turned towards her. This unnerved Judy so much that she then ran from the room.

Tim had hardly entered the house when he was actually pounced upon by Judy. Her arms encircled him so tightly and unexpectedly that he was knocked backwards against the wall. Even the couple's tender love for each other did not usually encompass quite such a vigorous greeting, so Tim lost no time in enquiring what was wrong. His wife's face looked haggard as she related her story.

Following her quick retreat from the bedroom, she had been sitting in the living room hugging Michael for almost two hours, until she could stand the tension no more and decided to walk to the local store. Not that she needed to buy anything; it was more a case of occupying her thoughts, trying to rid herself of the memory of that frightening experience.

For hours she walked aimlessly round the different stores, and would have stayed out until Tim came home. But the weather started to become cold and wet, the stores would be closing soon, and Judy had no other option but to return to the house.

A look of pleading now joined the fear in her eyes. It prompted Tim into action. He stroked her hair and then ran up the stairs with the vibrancy of an avenging ghostbuster.

The closed door of the second bedroom, however, gave the impression of a barrier between the safe, sane world, and that of the bizarre and illogical. It made Tim stop suddenly, his hand pressed to the door handle. Minutes seemed to pass as he tried to decide if he should return to safety downstairs or enter into the unknown. But the memory of leaving his happy young wife that morning, only to return home to find her so alarmed, forced him on. He charged into the room with anticipation, ready to tackle any number of ghosts and ghouls. As the bedroom door vibrated on its hinges from his violent jolt, Tim stood in the room — alone.

About fifteen minutes later, Tim came wearily down the stairs and into the living room. Judy was sitting nervously on the edge of the settee. He sat down heavily beside her, letting his head fall into the back of the settee. Judy turned to him, silently awaiting his words. He looked at her weary face, then at her newly-bitten fingernails. He tried to reconcile his thoughts, but reconciliation would not come.

Attempting to sound at least somewhat rational, Tim told her there was nothing at all in the bedroom, nor anything inexplicable inside the wardrobe.

60

The only diversion from normality, he told her hesitantly, had been while he stood at the closed door: he could not dispel the overwhelming feeling that the bedroom was full of unearthly beings; he could almost hear them breathing, feel them pressing against the door from inside. Yet when he stepped inside, there was nothing but a plain, ordinary bedroom. And that unnerved him even more than the prospect of finding the room full of demons.

Judy was so distressed from her earlier experience, that she had not even given a thought towards the preparation of their evening meal. Tim was still confused by not seeing what he honestly expected to see. They sat together on the settee for almost thirty minutes before Tim finally remarked about them needing a change of scene, and suggested they collect a hamburger on the way to his parents' home: maybe they could offer some kind of explanation for all this.

Tim's parents sat quietly listening to the young couple as they related the events of that day. The television was on low and Tim's father kept casting a quick glance at it. No one noticed but Tim, for he was trying to ascertain their reaction to this weird tale told between mouthfuls of potato chips and beer. His mother looked as if she was lost in a daydream except for the occasional nod of her head.

When they had finished, there was a short silence. The young couple felt stilled with anticipation as they waited for comment.

Tim's mother broke the silence in acknowledgement to the validity of Judy's experience and, paying no attention to the reaction of the thunderstruck young couple, she went on to qualify her astonishing comment by recalling an episode from her past.

She must have been about ten years old, she told them, when she first noticed something odd about the wardrobe. They had been long since forgotten, but now the memories were slowly coming back.

The wardrobe had always been in her elder brother's bedroom. She was very close to Wayne, and they often talked together about all kinds of things. She remembered one day when Wayne had asked her to fetch his jacket from his bedroom, as they were going for a walk in the local park. She went into his room, took the jacket from the wardrobe, and was about to close its door and return downstairs when she noticed a shimmering light coming from the mirror.

The iridescent light she described, matched exactly that which Judy had seen, although what had appeared in the mirror on that occasion was a scene in which Tim's mother could see a small girl walking down a street. The girl then stopped to talk with an elderly couple who were mowing their lawn. The scene was intimately familiar to her. The street was the one in which she lived until she married, and the old couple, dear neighbours with whom she frequently passed the time of day. The little girl was indeed herself. The mirror, she deduced, was somehow repeating an event which

61

had actually occurred some five years previously; like it had been captured on film and shown at that moment, as if the mirror was some kind of television. She had been held in total fascination, not only by the scene itself, but also because it was reproduced in the most vivid and true colours, while television pictures of that time were produced only in black and white.

A cold chill ran through everyone's bones at this important revelation, and Tim noticed his father too was now giving his undivided attention.

Judy grasped the opportunity to ask if the old lady had pale yellow hair like the one she had seen. But their descriptions did not match in any respect.

Tim's mother immediately went on to say that the occasion had stuck in her mind for a number of years, and was the first of many such visions portrayed for her in the mirror. She explained about the old couple moving away to live with their son in Florida. She had been five years old at the time, so there was no doubt that the mirror had shown her a scene from her past.

Afterwards, while out walking, she had told her brother Wayne about the vision in his wardrobe mirror and was surprised to learn that he too had seen visions and also witnessed ghostly visitors in the night who would spend considerable time preening themselves in front of the same mirror.

For many years, both she and Wayne had secretly shared these strange mysteries of the mirror. But despite her familiarity with the old wardrobe, she could not offer any explanation for the phenomena, then or now.

When Wayne joined the army, she regularly sat for hours in his bedroom just gazing into the mirror, waiting for the next vision to appear. It had helped to distract her from the depressions of the war, at least for a little while.

But the depressions of war did eventually catch up with her one day in Wayne's bedroom. She had volunteered to keep her brother's bedroom cleaned and polished in readiness for his return.

In the middle of polishing the set of drawers in Wayne's bedroom, her attention had been caught by the familiar light coming from the wardrobe. She stopped polishing and went to the mirror, anxious to see what would be revealed.

As the coloured haze cleared, she saw what was obviously a battle scene. People in uniform were running amid smoke and enemy fire. They were American troops, she recognised the uniform. As she watched, she suddenly became aware of someone with familiar features: it was Wayne. He was there running with the others. Tanks were rumbling past, firing their guns, as if charging the enemy.

She was completely engrossed in the scene, and had to remind herself not to alarm her parents by loudly cheering the troops on.

She whispered her cheers, although knowing they could not be heard by the men inside the mirror. Enemy fire increased and it was difficult to follow the men through the explosive flashes and smoke. Then, she lost sight of Wayne. She peered at the scene trying to find him again.

As the smoke cleared, she found Wayne. He had been wounded. He was staggering forward, his gun trailing on the ground. Then he fell and lay still.

She knew then, that he was dead.

With Tim's father holding her tightly, she fought through the tears to finish her story.

All the visions had been pleasant before then, and it gave her a severe shock to witness the death of her brother so unexpectedly. She tried to tell herself the mirror had lied, that Wayne was alive. Yet, the mirror had always been true when it portrayed the past, and the future.

It was nearly two months later when her parents were notified that Wayne had been killed in action.

Perhaps it had lessened her shock, because she had already accepted Wayne's death. But she still felt resentful towards the mirror. It had been the last vision she saw, as she never went near the wardrobe after that. The last forty-four years had eroded the memory of the visions in the wardrobe mirror until just now when Judy proved they were still active.

Her mother-in-law's story sent cold shivers through Judy. Then she remembered there were plenty of offers to take the old wardrobe off their hands. She wondered if the offers were still open.

The Hanged Man

When one is familiar with the paranormal, it is not unusual to assume that one is immune to psychic phenomena, because it always then appears to happen to someone else. However, it is impossible to make such guarantees, as David, a member of IPR found to his amazement. His advantage of having instant access to all the available resources only lessened the shock slightly, and for the most part he and his wife underwent the same turmoil that might be expected of any other percipient.

PARANORMAL EXPERIENCES OFTEN cause people to move home, but occupants are also driven out by other than supernatural phenomena. Sometimes, the simple suggestion of phantom beings is more bizarre than the reality of a substantiated haunting, and has caused almost as many homes to be just as wantonly abandoned.

Shortly after David Poole and his wife Margaret, moved into an old house in the suburbs of Wrexham, Wales, they noticed many strange noises such as doors slamming and furniture being dragged across bare floorboards. They could not find any explanation for this, as none of the furniture was ever moved, and the house was carpeted throughout.

Sometimes either David or Margaret would catch a fleeting glimpse of the ghost-like figure of a woman passing a doorway, rounding a corner or walking across the room in which they sat. She appeared to be under thirty years old, slim, with dark hair and wearing a simple dress, often worn with an apron. The sightings lasted for only a second or two, but were frequent enough to gain an approximate description of the apparition.

The couple's first thought was that whatever they were experiencing seemed very real, though they could not comprehend how it was possible to hear such noises without the corresponding movement of the doors or furniture; nor could they comprehend the fleeting visions of the young woman who appeared in various parts of the house.

She would always appear suddenly and walk a few steps before

64

vanishing, as if she was walking past an open doorway which viewed another world, yet the varied locations of her sighting would require several doorways scattered throughout the house, or one which was able to move at will.

They had not mentioned anything of the phenomena to their neighbours, and it was strange in itself that only at this time did the neighbours begin spontaneously to mention the ghostly tales concerning the house.

This unsolicited information was conveyed in a very casual manner: Margaret would perhaps be walking to the shops and someone would call to her from across the road, then come running over to her, asking how they were settling in and say, 'Of course, the house is haunted you know. It has quite a reputation . . .'

It was this reputation that actually destroyed any chance of peace for David and Margaret.

Apparently, their house was once owned by a man hereafter referred to as Mr W., who allegedly came home unexpectedly one day and found his wife in bed with her lover. Mr W. was so enraged by the scene that he killed his wife and buried her near an ancient dyke not far from the house.

What the lover was doing during the time of the slaying, and what eventually happened to him, is not known.

The legend goes on to say that Mr W. was found hanging from a tree in the front garden a year later. The tree was subsequently chopped down for its part in the evil suicide, or possibly to rid the community of a constant reminder of those dark deeds.

Given the sightings of a ghostly young woman in the house, David and Margaret found it difficult to ignore the eerie reputation. It seemed to fit in so well. They had no wish to believe it, and would have preferred to forget all about it. But from then on, every time they saw the lady ghost it was to serve as a reminder of the sinister tale of the hanged man.

Margaret became uneasy whenever she was alone in the house and soon, she started badgering David about selling the evil house and moving as far away as they could.

After several months, David had to admit that their growing unease presented a better case for moving than any other reasons could for staying. But he was sure it was all just a local tale made up from fictitious nonsense, and with not an ounce of fact in it. The main problem about moving was a financial one. They had just bought new carpets throughout, then there would be all the moving expenses again, and who knows how much money they would lose on the sale. The house had been on the market for a long time before they bought it, and there was every indication that they would be forced to sell for thousands of pounds less that they had paid for it, if they were to move out quickly.

David seriously weighed the situation in his mind for two whole days before a brilliant idea came to him.

He was determined to prove once and for all that the reputation was unfounded, and what better way to do it than by digging up the front garden where the tree was said to have existed. If the tree ever did exist, there were bound to be some roots still left in the ground and he intended to dig a hole so deep and so wide that nobody could seriously believe there was ever a tree there. And more importantly, he could also prove to his wife that there was no evidence to support such a ridiculous story. Margaret agreed that she would not be as eager to sell the house if indeed there were no remains of a tree.

After a considerable amount of exhaustive digging on a cold and windy summer's afternoon, David had dug down to a depth of sixty centimetres at the appointed spot in the front garden. With the back of his hand, he wiped the sweat from his brow. It was replaced immediately by a different kind of sweat, a nervous sweat as he struck something hard with his spade. He looked down into the hole at the uncovered roots and partial stump of a tree.

It was this discovery that scared both himself and Margaret more than anything else, for every time they walked through the front garden the thought of the tree and its hanging corpse made their flesh creep.

Mr W. did in fact live in the house thirty years previously, which adds a powerful credence to the legend, although little is known of the man or his life.

The ghostly lady, the sounds of doors slamming and furniture moving, were all proved authentic. Whether they are actually connected with the story of Mr W., will probably never be known.

And while David and Margaret were not disturbed by their lady ghost, the thought of a man hanging from a tree in their front garden, whether true or false, proved too much to bear, and they promptly vacated the house.

Jealous Wife

This case illustrates how the interaction of preternatural events can create a situation where a husband and wife, very much in love, are in effect living in entirely different worlds. Also, the wife in the case has not only to cope with the bizarre world of the supernatural, but is forced by convention to try to ignore her trauma in order to return to the normal world for the benefit of her husband, who has no suspicion of the danger his wife is in. The case is unusual owing to the intense motive of the ghost.

EVERYTHING HAD HAPPENED so quickly over the past few months. Harmony, a widow in her early forties, never expected to meet, fall in love with, and marry Byron, a kind, generous man about ten years older than herself, and then move from Atlanta, Georgia, to Memphis, Tennessee, to live in his luxurious home. She could only describe it as a whirlwind fairytale romance.

She was at first worried that Byron had not fully recovered from the death of his first wife Marisa, almost a year earlier, but there were no signs of him still being in mourning. His business required him to travel extensively throughout the United States, so there was no time for him to stand still and bury his head in the sand.

It was late Sunday evening when they arrived home in Memphis from their honeymoon in Mexico. This was the first time Harmony had seen the large house in which they were to live together. Byron gave her a guided tour, then they ate a light meal and retired for the night.

Byron reminded her that he always left early for work, but was accustomed to taking care of himself, so Harmony was not to trouble herself getting out of bed with him unless she particularly wished to. He had arranged to come home for the first few days to make sure everything was alright, but after that she was only likely to see him for three days each week.

Harmony awoke shortly before nine o'clock. She would probably have stayed in bed longer, still being tired after the flight, but the shock of the previous night's experience disturbed her a little. Had she not known that Byron's first wife was dead, she would have sworn Marisa still lived in the house, as Byron had not touched one item of her belongings. They were all left just as they probably were before she died.

The first clues to strike Harmony's attention were the hairbrushes and make-up neatly displayed on the dressing table. Then, as she was about to unpack, she found drawers full of Marisa's lingerie, the closet full of her dresses, coats and shoes. Harmony was astounded, and in the end only hung a few choice items of her own which she could manage to squeeze into the closet, the rest of her clothes remaining still packed in a case on the floor of the dressing room. Finally, as they were climbing into bed, there, at her side of the bed, she saw Marisa's bedroom slippers.

Harmony reviewed the situation this Monday morning. She felt compassion for Byron. Obviously, he had not been able to face the task of going through his late wife's clothes. But she was surprised that the maid did not volunteer to do it: Tonya came in once a week to do the cleaning chores throughout the whole house. Had she been afraid to mention the matter to Byron? Had she even seen him to ask about it? Byron would have been away on Fridays when Tonya came in to clean, and it was far too delicate a matter simply to leave a memo asking if she could get rid of his dead wife's personal possessions.

On reflection, Harmony thought it too delicate to mention the previous night, otherwise she would have said something about it then, instead of letting it play on her mind as she struggled to fall asleep.

The thought of Tonya cleaning and polishing the dressing table, then neatly replacing Marisa's hairbrushes and make-up, sent a cold shiver down Harmony's spine.

Whatever the reason for Marisa's clothes being left as they were, Harmony was now Byron's wife and she had her *own* dresses to hang, lingerie to put in drawers, and bedroom slippers for the side of the bed. In a few days she would bring the rest of her clothes from her house in Atlanta, and as she had nothing else planned for the day, there was no reason not to take on the task of dispensing with Marisa's clothing herself.

After breakfast, Harmony made a mental inventory of Marisa's personal possessions. Then she went to the local store for some groceries and a large box. She returned with the largest one she could find. It would not hold everything of Marisa's, but at least it was a start in the right direction.

There were several things she asserted could simply be thrown away, but others, especially the framed photograph of Byron and Marisa, she was not sure what to do with. She finally took it from the display case in the dining room and placed it in a drawer, intending to ask Byron about it later.

Upstairs and feeling like an intruder, Harmony began at the dressing table, where the most obvious of the offending articles had been the cause of her initial shock.

Carefully and meticulously, she placed the make-up and brushes into the box. Occasionally, a bottle of perfume would catch her eye and she would open it and test the elegant scent; she liked the fragrances, but could not imagine herself buying them: they were just not her style, or her price.

The top of the dressing table looked naked now, and she stopped momentarily to look at it with approval, and then started on the drawers. Before long, she began to think that it was such a waste to throw them out: everything was of the best quality, most were either new or almost new. She decided to check later if a charity would take them.

The dressing table emptied, Harmony turned to the closet opposite. It was huge, built into the full length of one wall of the dressing room, and about four metres wide. There were three sets of hinged double doors in heavy panelled wood. Harmony opened the doors at one end and started taking the less dressy clothes off their hangers. She noticed that Marisa took the same size as herself and, here too, most of the garments had designer labels.

Soon the box was full, clothes neatly folded and stacked well above its rim. But she had not made much of an impression at all, only relieving the closet of the at-home dresses; there were still the day and evening dresses, skirts and blouses, coats, shoes, hats, etcetera, which still occupied more than three quarters of the closet.

After lunch, Harmony decided to transfer the remaining clothes to the large second bedroom.

Although her first inclination was to clear all of Marisa's clothes out of the master bedroom as quickly as possible, now she found herself setting aside a few choice items that she was tempted to keep for herself.

With a twinge of excitement, Harmony quickly slipped off her own dress and tried on a beautiful, cream silk blouse and coral linen skirt. Standing in front of the full-length mirror in the second bedroom, she looked at herself from all angles; it was a perfect fit and decidedly more elegant that Harmony's usual apparel.

Throughout the afternoon, Harmony tried on many dresses, blouses, skirts and coats that she liked, all of which she put together at one side of the closet.

Time flew by, the closet became full and Harmony had to start filling the closet in the smaller third bedroom. In her attempt to be finished in time for Byron's arrival, she had to resort to making a mental note of clothes she would like to try on when next she had the house to herself.

In the end, she had to interrupt the task to prepare the meal.

When everything was in readiness for Byron's arrival, she returned upstairs to move more clothes from her closet.

She had just carried fifteen or so outfits to the closet in the small bedroom, when a dress slipped from her grasp to the floor. It was a beautiful deep blue, with gold threads twinkling throughout the fabric. Byron would be home any minute, but she could not resist trying on the dress.

Once more she stripped, stepped into the blue evening dress and zipped it up. Glancing in the mirror, it looked slightly too large around the bust and waist without its belt, which she then picked up from the floor. But instead of it going around her waist, she found herself putting it over her head and around her neck – pulling it tighter and tighter until she was gasping for breath.

Her hands did not seem to be her own any more and Harmony had to fight with all her strength to regain control, and finally she managed to throw the belt to the floor.

She massaged her painful neck as she gulped in the sweet air. She was shocked, confused, hurt, and repulsed by seeing the reflection in the mirror of her own two hands trying violently to strangle her.

Quickly she took off the dress and tossed it on the bed. Then she realised her own dress was not on the bed where she had left it. She looked all over the floor, and eventually found it, crumpled in a heap underneath the bed, as if someone had spitefully thrown it under there.

As she was stepping into her own dress again, she heard Byron's car outside on the driveway. She raced around bringing the few remaining clothes to the small bedroom, and finally she put the blue evening dress and its belt back on a hanger in the closet and closed the door. She carried the packed box into the large second bedroom, then remembering about the bedroom slippers, quickly grabbed them and stuffed them into the box and tried to compose herself as she descended the stairs to greet her husband.

During dinner, she raised the subject of Marisa's personal possessions, without reference to her experience with the blue dress: she did not want Byron to think he had married an unbalanced woman, as she was having a difficult enough time trying to understand what had happened to her.

Byron asked if he could leave their fate in Harmony's capable hands, explaining that he had never known what to do about them and being away from home so much, procrastination developed and, finally, he simply ignored them. A few old photographs were all he wanted to keep.

Later, when they went upstairs for the night, Harmony's strange experience with the blue dress seemed like a dream, a horrible dream, but a dream nevertheless. The time spent relaxing with Byron had distanced her from the terror she felt earlier, and now she really could not believe that it actually happened. She felt good about what she had accomplished that day and was happy to be hanging her own few clothes in the vacant closet.

It was at this point, when she walked towards the bed, that shock once more hit her, as she stared in disbelief at Marisa's bedroom slippers at the side of the bed.

Harmony remembered taking them into the second bedroom, putting them in the box. She was certain of that. But if that was so, how could they still be by the bed? Quickly, she picked them up, marched to the second bedroom and placed them in the box where they lay neatly in the indentation against the stack of clothes.

When Byron came from the bathroom, Harmony was in bed with the sheets pulled up to her chin, apparently restful, yet her mind in turmoil.

The following day, Harmony awoke early in the afternoon. She had slept badly, and woken up several times during the night. When she stumbled out of bed, there again were Marisa's bedroom slippers. Harmony was too weary from her lack of sleep to be shocked this time, but after she had showered and dressed, she took the bedroom slippers straight down to the trash can and slammed the lid on them defiantly.

During lunch, she reflected over the bizarre events. It was possible she was mistaken about placing Marisa's bedroom slippers in the box the first time, but surely not a second time. And yet they had found their way back to the bedroom somehow. Byron certainly would not have put them there; he obviously had not moved anything of Marisa's since she died. In fact, he did not even seem to notice that Harmony had moved them. But what of herself? They were her own two hands that put the belt around her neck after all. Was it possible that, during the night, she had left the bed to retrieve Marisa's bedroom slippers and then not remembered having done so? Harmony just did not know.

Clearing away the dishes, she noticed faint dark shadows which appeared then disappeared in different areas of the combined kitchen and breakfast room. Suddenly, she became weak and fell to her knees, grasping the nearest chair for support. Her stomach seemed to rise up inside then dizziness, panic and a sensation of falling.

Harmony gripped the chair with all her might, until finally she felt strong enough to drag herself into the living room and sit in an easy chair. She still felt weak as she closed her eyes for a moment's relaxation.

She awoke suddenly to the slam of a door. The greeting which followed, assured her it was Byron. She looked at her watch, and could hardly believe that it was now almost seven o'clock: she had been asleep in the chair for more than five hours, from which she felt stiff. And she had not prepared anything for their evening meal.

71

Byron seemed to take the situation with his usual equanimity, suggesting they go out for dinner instead. Harmony was still surprised by his apparent calmness after being out travelling all day, but was nevertheless grateful for his understanding. Her illness seemingly gone, she went upstairs to shower and dress while Byron poured himself a drink in the living room.

It was in the dressing room, looking into the almost empty closet, that she realised she *literally* had nothing to wear. All her evening clothes were either waiting to be laundered, after their honeymoon, or still at her house in Atlanta.

She returned downstairs to inform Byron of her predicament. He calmly suggested she wear one of Marisa's outfits, providing they were still in the house of course, and if Harmony had no objection.

Harmony was reluctant at first, but there was no other choice, she needed something to wear and Marisa had an abundance of evening wear.

At the closet in the large second bedroom, she searched quickly through the garments which had previously appealed to her. She found the pearl grey, velour dress and white fur coat which matched the mental picture that had come into her mind when she entered the room. Within minutes, she was dressed and 'ready for action'!

They were just finishing the main course of their meal when Harmony felt a mild pain. It was more of a tightness, a crushing feeling across her chest. At first she thought the dress might be a little too restrictive, but this was not the case, there being plenty of room for movement. The pain steadily increased through dessert, and now it was really hurting her. She had suffered it for over twenty minutes. It was persistent, with sudden sharp pangs, and felt like she was being crushed by the dress, as if it was somehow shrinking across the front, with her inside, like a great weight pressing into her. It seemed to limit her intake of air: her lungs were not fully able to expand. And she was unbearably hot, which alone made her breathing laboured.

Somehow she struggled through the evening, fighting the pain, the heat, and unconsciousness. Only when she was home, after removing the dress with great difficulty in the bathroom, did she begin to recover from her terrible ordeal. To aid her recovery, although still in her lingerie, she leaned her head into the shower stall and turned on the cold tap. She sighed with relief as she bent low and let the water run over her head and upper chest. It was uncomfortable, but refreshingly cool.

Harmony felt much better the next day, Wednesday. Byron and herself spent most of the day at her own house in Atlanta, which was now to become their second home. They gave the whole house a thorough cleaning, covered the furniture, and made sure the house was secure. Harmony collected more of her clothing, and her car.

The illness returned with a vengeance the following day, but Harmony managed to fight off the worst of it by keeping busy. In the afternoon, she went into the centre of Memphis to familiarise herself with her new surroundings and buy groceries. She felt great while she was out.

By eight o'clock that evening, she felt so weak that she retired early. It was her first night alone in the house and it was the most awful night she had ever known. Tossing and turning, she woke then slept, all through the night. She had nightmares, saw blurred visions and heard muffled voices. When she awoke just after eleven o'clock on Friday morning, she felt an absolute wreck. It was only at noon when Tonya called to her from downstairs, that she gathered the energy to get out of bed.

She gave only vague recognition to her scattered make-up on the dressing table and all her clothes lying on the floor of the closet instead of hanging from the rail. What surprised her was that she was *not* surprised; as if she had somehow expected it. The only thing she could remember clearly about the previous night, was the vision of Marisa standing over the bed, as if she was still alive.

Entering the kitchen downstairs, Harmony registered the momentary shock on Tonya's face, and knew instantly that it was due to her own zombie-like appearance. So much for first impressions, thought Harmony. But Tonya introduced herself with a warm greeting and a smile, offering to make Harmony a cup of coffee and some brunch. Harmony settled for the coffee, and soon felt at ease with Tonya and her light, cheerful conversation.

After several cups of coffee, Harmony asked about Marisa. Tonya proved to be very informative and told her many details obviously gained through long conversations with the former mistress of the house. Some of the details seemed to awaken an acknowledgement in Harmony's confused mind.

Marisa had died in a plane crash, and as Tonya explained what happened, Harmony realised her own symptoms were similar to those which Marisa must have experienced just prior to her death: the stomach seeming to rise up, the feeling of falling, the dizziness and panic, the sensation of being crushed, and immense heat.

Tonya told of Marisa being a very possessive woman. She could not bear for Byron to as much as look in the direction of another woman. Harmony was surprised that Marisa did not object to Byron spending so much time away from home, but Tonya assured her there was not a hint of jealousy on that score as far as she was aware. But then, Marisa had an intimate knowledge of Byron's business affairs and would have been the first to defend him against allegations of infidelity.

The afternoon passed quickly. Harmony had sorted and delivered all but a few of Marisa's clothes, leaving the ones she really liked in the small bedroom closet. When she returned, Tonya had already tidied the dressing table, cleaned the house and gone home.

Harmony felt rather pleased with herself by the time Byron arrived home, and they spent a restful and quiet weekend together.

On Monday morning, all hell seemed to break loose. Harmony was roused from her slumber by the closet doors crashing and grating against each other as they swung back and forth. She sat bolt upright in bed, then cautiously approached the dressing room to see what was happening. Her clothes were strewn about the room, her make-up was also on the floor. All the drawers of the dressing table were fully opened and her lingerie scattered throughout the dressing room as if propulsed from the drawers by an explosion. Both the dressing room and bedroom were icy cold. Gradually the closet doors stopped swinging, and all was quiet in the house. Harmony listened for some minutes to the silence. She knew Marisa was responsible for this vendetta and shouted aloud to be left in peace. Again she listened as if for a reply, but there was none.

Harmony was a resilient woman, who, despite everything, tried to carry on her life the best she could. But from this time, her second week in the house, the situation developed the unmistakable characteristics of a severe haunting.

Harmony's fits of high temperature, dizziness and pain, came and went spasmodically over the ensuing weeks. A medical checkup revealed nothing, and further tests at the hospital concluded that she was in perfect health.

In fact, most things were perfect while Byron was at home. Yet within fifteen minutes of him leaving for work, Harmony would waken to fervent poltergeist activity of one kind or another, which would come and go at will throughout the day.

One morning, Harmony awoke to a loud banging sound coming from downstairs but when she went downstairs, the noise stopped. She was tired and not particularly fond of waking up to loud noises, especially before seven o'clock in the morning. The dark shadows appeared again, this time following her about the house, and she could hear an intermittent buzzing sound inside her head. When she wearily went upstairs to lie on the bed for a while, the bedroom door was jammed closed and no matter how she tried, she could not open it.

Other days brought similar inexplicable frustrations. They were always prolific when Harmony was alone in the house, and conspicuously so on Mondays and Thursdays. Whenever Byron was at home, on Wednesdays and at the weekend, or on Friday afternoons when Tonya came in to clean, usually only the illness and minor irritations persisted. Otherwise, for three days each week, Harmony was tormented by the sinister intimidations of the phenomena.

74

Every single day, an overpowering smell of what Harmony recognised as one of Marisa's perfumes would emanate from inside the dressing table drawers, her closet, and the one in the small bedroom containing the few clothes belonging to Marisa. Sometimes, Harmony would catch the scent of it as she moved about the house, particularly in the bedroom and living room.

The bedroom door frequently would not open when Harmony tried to enter, though it opened easily for anyone else. The bathroom door jammed in the same way, while the doors to the other bedrooms refused to open from the inside but were easily opened when Harmony entered.

In Byron's absence, Harmony had to sleep in one of the spare bedrooms on the occasions that she could not gain entrance to her own. But she always made sure the door was wedged open after one frightening episode when she found herself trapped in the room all morning. Even this ploy was not to be completely relied upon, as she still occasionally awoke in the morning to discover the door closed and jammed.

Often she would go to bed and the bedroom light refused to work, although once she was in bed, it would come on by itself. Her clothes were frequently found on the closet floor as if they had simply slipped from their hangers; or were strewn across the dressing room and bedroom floors. Her make-up was swept from the dressing table every day that Byron was not at home. By now, she had learned to distribute her clothing and other necessities between the two large bedrooms as well as other locations throughout the house in anticipation of sleeping wherever it was permitted by – she was certain – Marisa. But still every morning she awoke to find clothing and make-up on the floor of whichever room she slept in.

Finally, Harmony told Tonya of her ordeal, naming Marisa as the cause. Tonya was not as surprised as she might have been; apparently, ever since Marisa's tragic death, she had seen her ghost every week and lately Marisa had often turned to smile at her, not a sweet smile, but a knowing, devilish smile. Tonya did not understand at the time, but now she could see the significance.

Harmony did not know many people in Memphis to whom she could turn for help, nor was she sure anyone would believe all that had happened to her. For that reason, she had never mentioned the matter to her family when she wrote. Tonya, however, had lived in the area for most of her life and assured Harmony she would find out what could be done.

The following week and purely by chance, Tonya arrived two hours earlier than usual on Friday morning, and entered the house to the sound of Harmony kicking and screaming at something upstairs. Tonya immediately ran upstairs to find Harmony seemingly locked in the second bedroom, an overturned chair resting at the top of the stairs. Tonya turned the handle, opened the door, and Harmony rushed from the room in tears.

Tonya had arrived early to tell Harmony of some good news. She had made provisional arrangements for a medium to come to the house and hopefully quieten Marisa's spirit.

The medium came and went, to no avail.

Next, they had the house blessed – twice. But Marisa proved stubborn.

Then came another medium who claimed to be an expert at exorcism and a TV personality, *and* charged a suitably large fee. After two attempts in forty minutes, she assured the two women that all was safe and Marisa would trouble the house no more. Later that night, all the light bulbs shattered, and if anything, Harmony's illness grew worse.

Another medium came and went. Then a clairvoyant. Nothing seemed to rid the house of Marisa's influence, and they were now running out of ideas, although Marisa seemed to have an abundance of them, as they were later to discover.

Harmony was also becoming worried that the next knock on the door might be news reporters. She did not need this. So far she had been able to keep the whole situation a secret from Byron, and certainly did not want him reading in the newspaper over breakfast about how she had been trying to rid the house of his late wife's ghost.

This, however, became a very real probability when Harmony overheard two women talking about the haunting in one of the local stores. She was now forced to tell Byron, before someone else did.

Byron, as could be expected, was a little dubious about the story he heard. He had never seen Marisa's ghost, and felt that if she had somehow returned from the grave, he would surely be the first to know about it. However, faced with the insistence of Harmony and Tonya, Byron promised to look into the possibility of seeking someone qualified to help.

Meanwhile, the disturbance was becoming dangerous and malicious.

Tonya had just arrived at noon on Friday, when once more, every light bulb in the house shattered. This time, the vacuum cleaner would not work, and the two women had to clean up the tiny fragments of glass using brushes. They were still feverishly brushing when Byron came home.

The following week, furniture started to roll across the floor to crash into Harmony. Tonya too became a target whenever she was in the house.

Every day now, Harmony awoke to find her make-up and clothing scattered over the carpet, even when Byron was at home. Frequently, electrical appliances failed to work when Harmony switched them on, and loud noises and crashes were heard through-out the house at various times of the day and night.

Sometimes, while alone or with Tonya, Harmony had to suffer through a whole day or more without any electrical power at all. Amazingly, the power was always restored the instant Byron came home. At which, the refrigerator immediately started to rapidly cool its contents and within seconds had regained its normal operating temperature, though much of the food inside had to be discarded. Subsequently, only necessary items were kept in there, and Harmony made a point of buying any refrigerated items for the evening's meal, late in the afternoon.

Harmony was beginning to hate staying in the huge house alone, so was relieved to think that she might have company one day on hearing a knock at the door. She opened the door with anticipation, and almost died of shock at the sight of Marisa standing in front of her, smiling! It was a wry smile. That, and a fawn fur coat were all that impinged on Harmony's mind before she froze, her mouth wide open. Marisa looked so real, so alive. Eventually, Harmony man-aged to force her body to move and stumbled back inside the house, slamming the heavy wooden door closed, her body slumped against it. She expected Marisa to knock at the door again, but she did not. Harmony remained against the door for what seemed an eternity, hardly daring to breathe, not wanting to believe what she had seen, but unable to deny it.

Later that week, when Harmony had almost recovered from her terrible fright, she again answered a knock at the door to find Marisa staring back at her. Harmony screamed, slammed the door closed and ran upstairs in tears. After that time, Harmony refused to answer the door to anyone.

On Friday, Tonya was attending to her regular chore of cleaning out the fireplace, when suddenly, soot poured down from the chim-ney, covering much of the room, and herself. The vacuum cleaner, which had been working just minutes earlier, now would not work. Again Byron returned home to find the two women laboriously brushing up the dirt.

Through his business associates, Byron eventually heard of an accountant in New Jersey who, many years ago, had been troubled by a poltergeist running riot in his offices. Hence, a few discreet enquiries brought Byron to The Institute for Psychical Research.

The team of investigators were soon able to confirm the haunting. They discovered too, that Harmony's health problem was only evident either inside the house or whenever she wore any of Marisa's clothes outside. Medical examinations performed at the time of the investigation attest to the reality of the symptoms.

A completely new aspect of the haunting came to light at this time. Chairs started falling over onto the floor directly in front of someone walking past, causing them to trip. This happened twice to investigators and once to Harmony.

On Friday, when Tonya screamed from the direction of the living room, everyone rushed to her assistance, finding her sprawled in the fireplace covered in soot and with an upturned occasional table on the carpet nearby. She had been cleaning the grate when she received a sudden impact to her behind, which sent her careering headlong into the fireplace. She banged her head on the back wall and then the soot thundered down on top of her. The occasional table was normally located on the opposite side of the living room, and Tonya could offer no explanation of how it had moved or if it was that or something else which sent her crashing into the fireplace. Again the vacuum cleaner refused to work, although it worked perfectly when connected to a socket in another room.

The phenomena had taken such a strong hold, that a qualified exorcist was required in order to restore peace and tranquility to the house.

When Byron arrived home, tentatively calling Harmony's name, he found everyone relaxing in the now clean living room, talking laughing and drinking tea. Harmony, for the first time, was starting to enjoy her new life with Byron in their luxurious home. And from the greeting she gave him, it looked as if she had cooked up a real surprise for dinner, at which the investigators decided it was time to leave the two of them alone. After all, if three was a crowd, nine certainly was.

Cultured Vegetation

A popular misconception about the paranormal is that a ghost will return to a place where it experienced some intense emotion. The correct statement should read 'can' not 'will', and the same rule applies to attachment to objects as much as to places. Although the following two cases are of similar hauntings, their differences are notable. Each case was reported by the mother of the child involved. The first case echoed the question: 'Is this really happening?' and the mother was not exactly thrilled to have the phenomena confirmed. The second case was decidedly: 'Come and look what is happening!' and the whole family were ecstatic at the confirmation.

FLOWERS ARE INDEED a strange commodity. For thousands of years they have been associated with death, and rebirth; sadness, and joy; apology, and celebration. The following cases, which are individually remarkable experiences, seem to show how easily the natural and supernatural worlds can merge. Both cases have the similar theme of a flowering plant symbolising a gift of friendship.

At ninety-two years of age, Edith Butler was just as active in her beautiful garden, as she had been seventy years before. The tall, stout woman also made her own way on foot to the nearby shops twice a week, a trip which she made as regular as clockwork and in all weathers. Only when her husband had died fifteen years previously, did she fail to do her own shopping. A niece had brought it three times, before the old lady refused to be 'treated like a child' and thereafter continued the routine herself.

She had no home help, nor did she want one. Her house was paid for and her savings over the years had amounted to enough to get by on. She knew nothing of pensions.

Everyone described her as the sweetest, most caring person they knew. This seemed a contradiction when judged by her sharp tongue alone. But one had to consider that her loud, concise commands contained no venom, and were accompanied by bright, friendly eyes and a loving smile. It was a type of kindly assertiveness which any unsuspecting person could easily misunderstand.

In many respects, Edith was isolated from the world around her. She seemed to live in another, long-forgotten time. But while the present day did not affect her own life, she was mindful of its toll on those close to her heart.

For every death which occurred in the Bristol, Avon, cul-de-sac, Edith never failed to present to the family in the grief-stricken household, the most lavish of wreaths made by her own fair hand, with flowers from her garden, and with the respect and consideration of the closest of friends.

Not one resident was married without Edith making a gift of money; nor one family would suffer if the wage-earner became ill and could not work, for Edith would take them parcels of food with the efficiency of a friendly, but busy delivery girl, never once accepting payment of any kind.

The one real love in Edith's life was her garden, and though she showed no obvious personal signs of being proud of it, she had immeasurable cause to be. She had started with nothing more than bare soil, and worked every day, creating a showpiece of horticultural delight. Come rain or shine, she missed not one day tending something in her garden, even if it was for only five minutes in the pouring rain.

Many of her plants were thought to be extinct, and there were countless others that would have required an expert to name. Wild flowers grew beside popular shrubs and unusual herbs of every species. There was no mistaking the fragrant aroma of Edith's garden: it was a landmark among botanical gardens.

The flowers were in their most glorious bloom during July of 1986, despite the lack of summer sunshine. Edith was cutting some flowers in her front garden, when young Diana stopped to say hello. She was a pretty little girl, just eight years old with long, blonde hair which curled naturally along its entire length.

Diana often stopped to talk with Edith as they both shared a closeness that was not easy to understand, given their age difference of 84 years. But Edith and Diana talked and laughed as though they had a secret rapport.

This day, the little girl showed anxiety for Edith's hard cutting of the flowers, but Edith told her not to worry and asked her to wait for a minute, after which she came back with a large bunch of freshly-cut weigela, saying that it was from her most favourite shrub.

The rosy pink flowers framed by dark green leaves atop thin whip-like stems took Diana's breath away. They were truly magnificent, as Diana promptly exclaimed.

Edith handed the bunch to her, firmly stating that they were her gift to the young girl, then sternly told her to be off and put them in some water. Diana could hardly contain the bulk of weigela in her arms and had to hold them against her body and face so she did not drop any.

That day, there was much talk among the neighbours of the old lady cutting every stem that bore a flower, to such an extent that her usually colourful garden was reduced to the drastic nakedness of winter. No one could deny their envy of Edith's colourful garden, but now they were appalled by its transformation.

The neighbours remained unaware of the fact that Edith died later that evening. She was found two days later, sitting in a chair in the lounge, completely surrounded by vases filled with the flowers from her garden. How she had managed on her own to arrange the wide, circular display of tightly-packed vases, defies explanation. Her daughter had to move them out of her way to reach Edith's restful body, and claimed later that it was such a touching sight, helping to minimise the shock of finding her mother dead.

Almost a week later at the funeral, one of each variety of flower was sentimentally tossed onto Edith's coffin as it lay in the ground. The rest of her floral garden – still as fresh as the day it was discovered by her body – later being placed over her grave.

It was six weeks after the funeral that Diana's weigela cuttings started to fade. She placed them tenderly on the compost heap with more than a hint of ceremony, and tears in her eyes.

The following May, Diana noticed a bright rosy pink colour amidst the compost. She scraped back the rotting waste to discover the cuttings had rooted and now laid bare all the shrub's beauty. The covering of compost had not hindered the profusion of leaves and flowers and it has remained in that location ever since, the most beautiful of shrubs and Diana's favourite.

Diana still talks and laughs with Edith, but now it is in the far corner of her garden by the weigela shrub.

An announcement to her mother that she would take the shrub with her when she grows up and gets married was met with both sadness and relief. For while Diana's mother will miss her little girl, she certainly will not miss the shock she receives when a familiar sharp tongue lavishes horticultural advice on her when she is in the garden.

* * * *

In El Paso, Texas, Lila Rosario had a considerable struggle protecting her two Dwarf Stark Starlet peach trees from a very different kind of pest than aphids. His name was Larry, the ten-year-old boy who lived next door.

In true Texan style, Lila, in her late fifties, proudly displayed the one-metre tall peach trees on her patio, where they happily grew in containers, one on each side of the patio door.

The juicy peaches however, proved too much of a temptation for Larry and, although Lila bore him no malice, there were many running battles through the surrounding streets after Larry had attempted to help himself to her crop before they were even ripe. It seemed a futile game they played, but Lila felt good by giving chase and Larry felt good for having escaped. Despite their friendly feud, Larry helped Lila tidy her garden most weekends.

Early in the spring of 1971, Lila called on Larry and his parents to tell them she was going to Salt Lake City, Utah, the next day, to attend the funeral of her father. She asked if Larry would take care of her peach trees, making him promise not to pick the fruit until it was ripe, and to make sure he brought the trees inside during the winter. The young boy nodded his head in eager anticipation.

Larry's father, Bill, was astounded by her reference to winter and asked how long she planned to stay in Salt Lake. Lila replied that she was only going for two weeks, but wanted to ensure everything was taken care of before leaving, at the same time handing Larry written instructions for the care of the trees. Bill could only assume that she might stay in Utah longer, and assured her that Larry would take good care of the trees, jokingly adding that Larry would probably go over to check on their progress every single day after school.

At this, Lila started to become impatient, explaining that she did not want them left at her house, they were a gift to Larry and must be brought over to their house immediately. And she waited and watched as Bill carried the two trees from her house. Then she left to finish packing for the flight the next day.

Bill and his wife were confused by Lila's behaviour, but decided it was probably due to the shock of her father's death, and warned Larry that she might change her mind and want the trees back on her return.

It was over a month later when Lila's son visited Bill's house to inform them that Lila became ill, and subsequently died exactly two weeks after arriving in Salt Lake City.

The family were shocked to hear the sad news, but another, more severe shock was still to come.

As soon as Larry attempted to pick an unripe peach, he was admonished — by the ghost of Lila Rosario. Every time he tried, either alone or witnessed by his parents, Lila's ghost would materialise and shout at him with her usual, playful anger.

The haunting became quite a novelty during the next five years as Larry made his attempts to pick the fruit in a strange new game he played with Lila. After five years, the haunting stopped. But the lesson was well-learned and Larry has never picked an unripe peach to this day.

The Dedicated Nurse

Despite the percipient's initial report of this case being extremely accurate and well documented, one problem of investigating hauntings is highlighted by the fact that although the report was made within two weeks of the last occurrence, the actual start of the phenomena was about a year earlier and the percipient was the only eyewitness. But for his excellent report, we would have had very little to confirm the following detailed facts. The difficulties were considerably lessened by the percipients assistance in gaining entrance to the vacant house, before bulldozers destroyed further evidence.

NUMBER ONE, GREENBANK Terrace, is situated in an area where elite custom-built homes sit virtually cheek by jowl with less salubrious dwellings, as redevelopment year by year has taken its toll and many of the garden-fronted terraced houses have decreased their prominence in the busy, English market town. Greenbank Terrace, however, has so far survived, but it lacks its original dignity. Number One is no longer a nursing home for the elderly; it was vacated and sold to a local gentleman. He rented the property to the Chapman family, who had to beg, plead and threaten, in an effort to get repairs done, and despite Mrs Chapman's determination to brighten the home, it remained a dismal eyesore. The brickwork needed pointing, and many of the rooms were damp. Even the front garden would not sustain any plants other than the tenacious weeds and dusty laurel bushes.

Mrs Chapman was a widow, whose health could be fragile at times. Her two sons, Mark and George, both in their late thirties, were considerate and did their best to help around the house.

The Chapmans had lived in Greenbank Terrace for almost a year, when Mark began to experience various strange phenomena. He was the only member of the family to be plagued by this.

It began one night in November. Mark had not been feeling well that day and so came home early from work. That night, he was having difficulty getting to sleep. He felt so hot that he tossed off his blankets, despite the fact that the room was not heated and frost covered the ill-fitting sash window. Finally though, Mark fell asleep.

At sometime in the early hours of the morning, he began to hear muffled, female voices which intruded upon his deep slumber. He was too exhausted to fully wake himself, so the sound of women chattering nearby, quickly became no more than a background irritation to him. At one point, he recalled thinking that he wished they would shut up and leave him alone.

Then, hearing his own name whispered, he tried to rouse himself. It was hopeless, like trying to rise from some dark inky depth of partial unconsciousness. All he could do was try to concentrate on what the voices were saying. He managed to make out: 'He's not well, you know . . . Keep an eye on him . . . And see to those blankets, Nurse.'

The next moment, Mark felt his blankets being pulled over and tucked in all around him, the mattress actually lifting as this was done and his body rolling to a degree. Amazement registered in his fuddled brain, and then he dropped into a deeper sleep.

In the morning, when Mark awoke, he still felt unwell. He recalled lucidly all the details of the night before, and had to pull and tug to free himself from the blankets, which were well and truly tucked in around him. He was a large man, both tall and broad, which was why he was so amazed that some ghostly presence, if indeed that was what it was, had tucked him in with such practised ease during the night.

As Mark drank his morning tea in the kitchen, he asked his mother if she had been in his room the night before and tucked him in. Mrs Chapman, a compact little woman, laughed her denial, asking whatever had given him such an absurd idea. Not expecting an answer, she added that it was many a long year since she last tucked her Mark into bed.

Mark nodded his head, he had not imagined for a moment that she would say otherwise. After all, there had been at least two women in his room disturbing him with their chatter, and he recalled distinctly one calling the other 'Nurse'.

That night as Mark climbed into bed, feeling a little run down though better than he had the previous night, he wondered if there would be a repeat of the ghostly performance. He was so tired that he was soon asleep.

Again, it must have been during the early hours, when Mark was disturbed by the sound of female voices chatting. But there was no reference made to himself this time, nor was he tucked in as he was the night before, and after a short while he drifted into a deeper sleep.

As the weeks went by, Mark forgot about the strange experience, which he had not mentioned to his mother, or his brother George, for fear of being ridiculed.

Then, two weeks before Christmas, it happened again. Mark awoke to see a strange glow in one corner of his bedroom. It was a sort of pearl-grey and pale apricot colour. He was now fully awake, but his body felt as heavy as lead and he doubted his ability to spring out of bed should the need arise. As he stared at the luminous glow, a figure appeared in it, moment by moment becoming more visible, until Mark could make out every detail. It was a thin old man in a nightshirt, with a nightcap on his head. Mark wanted to laugh. He looked such a funny little chap. The old man then stood on a stool and seemed to be putting something over his head.

Mark gasped with alarm. The little chap was going to hang himself! But despite that one spontaneous inhalation, Mark was incapable of either speech or movement.

It was a huge relief when, the next moment, a lady appeared from the vicinity of the bedroom door. She was dressed in the unmistakable uniform of a nurse. A cool, assertive authority emanated from her. 'Now then, Mr Dexter,' she said. 'Come along, back to bed with you.' She held out her arms towards him. 'That's it, take my hand.'

Mark watched in a horrified fascination, as the little man, for a dreadful moment, seemed as if he would ignore her, but finally he did take her hand and she led him away, like one would a youngster who had been sleepwalking. The glow melted away and the room was once more in darkness.

The whole sequence from start to finish could not have lasted more than a couple of minutes. Mark, now apparently unrestricted, sat up in bed for a short while, thinking over what he had witnessed, until finally he got out of bed and went downstairs to make a hot drink. There would be no more sleep for him that night, and if this was to continue, he would find some excuse to swap bedrooms with George.

But Mark was left in peace for almost two weeks.

When the next manifestation occurred, it was even more disturbing as it took place during the cold, harsh light of day. It was Christmas Eve. Mark had finished work at lunchtime and came home to find his mother in the kitchen taking mince pies from the oven. There were already a couple of dozen cooling on the scrubbed table. Mark told his mother to sit down for a moment, and he would make them both a cup of tea.

As they drank their tea, Mrs Chapman told her son she would be having a night out for a change: a friend was picking her up around seven to take her to bingo.

Suddenly, Mark nearly dropped his mug of tea, for there behind his mother, stood the nurse. This phantom lady was shaking her head and all around her was a red glow. A moment later she was gone.

Mark stared at his mother, but it was obvious she had sensed nothing, she was still chatting away merrily about her plans for the evening. Taking the ghostly gesture to be a warning of some kind, Mark asked his mother if she was feeling alright. Mrs Chapman gave him a puzzled look, exclaiming that of course she was feeling alright, and asked if he thought that she looked ill. Mark assured her that she looked fine, but he just wondered if she might be better off stopping in by the fire and having a lazy evening rather than going out on such a freezing cold evening. But Mrs Chapman had no intention of missing out on the opportunity to go to bingo, especially as she would be taken there and brought back in a comfortable warm car.

As the evening wore on, Mark became more and more agitated. Ten o'clock came, then eleven, then midnight. Surely his mother should have been home by now!

When, just before one o'clock, there was a knock at the door, Mark knew his fears were about to be confirmed.

The uniformed policeman told Mark about the car accident and which hospital his mother had been taken to.

Mark went through the worst night of his life, thinking over and over of the nurse who had come with a warning, and wishing he had made his mother stay at home. Thankfully, Mrs Chapman recovered from her injuries and was back home three weeks later.

Spring came, then summer, and to Mark's intense relief, he saw and heard no more of the nurse or any others of the nursing home staff, or patients. Until, that is, one day in September.

It was a Saturday afternoon, and Mark was sitting comfortably in front of the television set, watching a sports programme. It was almost one o'clock, and time to switch channels to watch a particular match he was looking forward to. His mother was nodding off in her armchair, with a half-knitted pullover on her knee. His brother George was out, having gone to visit a lady friend in a nearby town. Mark was just wondering if he had enough time to make himself a cup of tea before the programme started, when there, standing beside the TV, was the nurse in her starched uniform.

Mark's blood ran cold. What disaster was impending this time, he thought. The very next second he heard an ungodly crunching sound, and actually leapt from his chair expecting the wall behind him to collapse. But not a thing was amiss in the room; the nurse had gone, his mother was still dozing in her chair and the programme he wanted to watch, was just starting.

When the policeman called later, to inform the Chapmans that George had been in an accident at one o'clock that afternoon, Mark was not surprised. George was not badly hurt and after being kept in hospital overnight, was allowed home.

Mark had had enough, and a month later the Chapman family moved out. Mark has never seen a ghost since, nor does he ever want to.

Manhattan Ghost Tour

A huge city like New York is enough to frighten many adults, and it was this knowledge alone that made the telephoned report by the percipient's brother appear at least partly believable. His report of Victoria's harrowing experience was laced with just a little more humour than one would expect; and for good measure, he added that his parents might disapprove of an investigation. Such problems are not uncommon. Another setback came when Victoria stated that there was nothing to tell, which was not far from the truth, considering she had no idea where she had been. An unexpected revelation emerged when the mocking brother shyly admitted to seeing the ghost in their home, though never outside. After more than a month since the event, it was not surprising that only two people came forward out of more than a thousand estimated possible witnesses. Neither of them saw the ghost, nevertheless they added valuable testimony. The kind young lady who stopped to enquire if Victoria was alright, may well have seen the ghost but, to date, she has still not been traced.

VICTORIA WAS FIFTEEN years old when her family relocated to New York city. She was disappointed about leaving all her friends, and especially having to decline an invitation to go with some of them to Florida where they planned to see Walt Disney World, and have the time of their lives with an almost continuous two-week party.

It was certainly not a good time for Victoria, no doubt other worries compounded the situation for the small-town girl, not the least of which were her school report and the usual adolescent problems, and now she had the prospect of having to make new friends, going to a new school after the summer break — and living in a strange, big city.

Her two elder brothers adapted well to their new life in Manhattan and considered it an exciting opportunity for their careers. But Victoria seemed to be hounded by one stressful situation after another. Her personality certainly changed as a result. No longer the sweet and open, happy young girl that she had once been, now she was irritable, argumentative, and spent most of her time locked in the complex labyrinth of her own private thoughts and worries. Her parents were so concerned by her behaviour that they were considering taking her to a psychoanalyst for therapy.

After about a week of her depression, she noticed out of the corner of her eye, a momentary, vague figure, that seemed to follow her from room to room in their Upper East Side home. She did not feel threatened by it, there were other more important issues than something which she could not properly see. Her friends, especially those living it up in Florida occupied her thoughts. They promised to write, but she could not imagine them finding the time for such a mundane chore if they were serious about their many plans for 'a great time'.

As Victoria became more depressed, the frequency of sighting the vague figure increased. No one but Victoria noticed it, but then everyone else in the family was busy working, or checking out the area and seeing the sights. Victoria always refused to go with them, growing more and more isolated in a strange city where she did not want to live.

When she did go outside during her second week, she stayed close to her home, walking the streets, her eyes open but her surroundings unnoticed. Sometimes she would sit for hours on the sidewalk, thinking about the small town where she grew up and about her friends enjoying themselves in Florida, while she herself was desperately sad and lonely.

It was during one of these occasions that Victoria realised that the unusual ghostly figure was standing outside in the street beside her. It was more distinct than before and seemed to be waiting for something. Victoria turned her head to look up at it, but it was suddenly not there anymore.

She reflected on her other sightings of the figure, but she had not paid much attention to it previously and had only vague recollections of the numerous occasions on which she had seen the figure over the past two weeks, though these had never been outside in the street. She had assumed their new home was haunted, but she was as disinterested in that as she was about living in Manhattan. The figure had been just another irritation before, but now it was even following her outside. It annoyed her because the figure seemed to disrupt her troubled thoughts and confuse her worried mind.

When she again felt and saw its presence, Victoria rose to her feet and walked away. But within ten minutes of sitting on the sidewalk a few blocks away, the figure was again standing beside her. This continued throughout the afternoon, Victoria walking away and the figure appearing beside her a short time later. Finally, frustrated at the figure's forced intrusion, Victoria returned home at about four o'clock, where the ghost sporadically continued to follow her from room to room.

In an attempt to escape its unwanted attentions, Victoria walked further away from home the next day. But soon she was aware of the figure continuously following her and when she turned round to look at it, she could now easily distinguish its outline enough to suggest it was the figure of a young man, though the features were still hidden. Her first instinct was to run, but this proved futile as he was always about four metres behind her. However, Victoria continued to walk then run alternately, with the figure silently following behind, driving her further and further into unfamiliar territory.

Then, she saw a bus about to move off and jumped on without any regard to its destination.

When she thought it was safe, she got off and continued walking until, several blocks later, she noticed the figure still following behind her. Once more, Victoria took the next bus she saw, then another, but within fifteen minutes of walking the streets again, the persistent figure was there.

Now she was really afraid of the unfamiliar city, for so engrossed was she in her attempt to escape from the figure, that she was now totally and irrefutably lost. The only indication of where she was, came from the knowledge that her bus journeys had taken her over two bridges, and that information did not even tell her if she was still in New York. It was certainly a busy city and she concluded that she was either in New York or Newark, New Jersey.

As she looked around her, she noticed that the figure seemed to be beckoning her. She ignored him and started walking briskly in the opposite direction, hoping that a street sign might give her some clue of her location. But they offered none: all had names which she did not recognise, and not one was a numbered street to give an indication of her geographical location in the city. She thought perhaps she was somewhere in the suburbs, but the congestion of traffic and the type of buildings did not confirm this.

Finally, she broke down in tears. A young woman noticed and asked if she was alright. Victoria muttered through the tears that a man was following her and she was lost and wanted to go home. Immediately realising Manhattan was now her home, she tried to correct herself by saying she did not want to go to 'that' home. But then, she had no other home to go to, and became so confused that the young woman probably could not understand what Victoria was talking about; and while her attention was focused on looking for the man who was following, Victoria suddenly ran away.

Somehow, she seemed to lose the ghostly figure and, turning a corner, immediately saw the New York County Court House directly opposite. She knew instantly she was in the right city, also, that she must be close to its centre. She looked for other significant landmarks and found the Criminal Courts Building not far away. She was now on Centre and walking towards the Criminal Courts Building, not sure if she was heading in the right direction, but determined to find her way home.

In less than twenty minutes she knew she was on her way home. She was relieved to see numbered streets now, and after passing East Eighth Street, she continued to walk northwards along Fourth Avenue for a short distance before realising her close proximity to the famous Fifth Avenue and, out of curiosity, promptly changed her route to include its dazzling sights. An hour later, she entered Central Park, her head constantly turning this way and that as she tried to see everything at the same time. She was mesmerised by the magical atmosphere of the city and could hardly believe she had walked past the Empire State Building. Continuing the full length of Central Park, her quest to reach home was now not as important as it had been earlier.

Leaving the park at East 110th Street, she wanted to turn round and start the tour again, but it was now getting late and she felt inclined to return home. It had been an exhausting day and her shoes were killing her.

When Victoria arrived home, her family were amazed by her ecstatic smile. One of her brothers, teasing about her dream-like state, remarked that she must have fallen in love. 'Yes!' Victoria confirmed, instantly throwing her arms around him and kissing him with such force that they fell to the floor in a fit of laughter. They struggled to their feet and Victoria proceeded to kiss and hug each of her family in turn. Her mother told her a postcard had arrived from Florida, but Victoria said she would look at it later. All she wanted to do right then was go to her bedroom to study the street map of New York which she had just bought, and plan where to go tomorrow. Her father asked where she had been today, and she responded by listing all the sights on her journey, adding how happy she was to be living in New York. He then asked what had happened to change her mind so suddenly. She replied that New York had taught her how to live in the present, instead of in the past; she quickly disappeared to her bedroom not wanting to mention the strange ghostly figure who had instigated the circumstances which forced her back to reality.

Time Stood Still

The ghost in this case took very little part indeed, although the phenomena around it would not have been possible without a ghost. Lori reported the phenomena just weeks later, because she wanted the occasion documented and preserved in the annals of psychical research to satisfy her deserved pride in the event. Lori was made fully aware of the implications of such an investigation: its first priority after all, is to confirm or deny the phenomena, a decision which becomes an extremely distinctive feature in the documentation and preservation of a case. Lori will be even more elated to see it recalled in this book, although she already knows it is not an unusual case; it is, however, unique in many respects.

STEPHEN HAD BEEN in the employ of the same company in Winnipeg, Manitoba, all his married life, and his consistency was as predictable as the passage of time itself.

When he retired, he still rose at six a.m. every morning without fail, but now he would take a long walk after breakfast, to return home at about nine o'clock when his wife Molly had woken. For the rest of the morning, he cleaned the whole house before sitting down to eat the lunch which Molly had prepared. In the afternoon, he worked in the garden and finally spent the evening relaxing in his chair, drinking beer and enjoying the companionship of his wife in just the same way that he had when he was working. The conversation had obviously changed, but nevertheless he still found interesting topics to discuss. Perhaps he had decided to clean out some drawers that morning, and discovered something which he had taken to be lost; or the sky was particularly beautiful during his morning walk; or he noticed the roof of their house was in need of repair, had made a note of the materials he needed and intended to make a start on the job at the weekend.

There was another side to their lives which was certainly not dull. In his youth, Stephen had travelled the world and always managed to make an abundance of friends, which, fifty years on, he still regarded as family. In fact, anyone who could name a friend of Stephen's, old or new, received the same consideration and was assured of a bed for the night and all that went with it. Stephen could be said to carry the warm Canadian hospitality to the extreme, and it was not unusual for a complete stranger to be staying in their house, borrowing the car, bringing other friends back, eating and drinking, and being treated like one of the family. Their two daughters were multi-lingual at an early age, learning to speak German, Spanish, Italian and several dialects of French while growing up.

Despite the house seeming to be like an international summer camp for foreign students at times, Stephen and Molly continued their lives with a happy balance of activity and calm.

At the weekend, there were still groceries to buy, jobs to be done around the house, and Stephen always cleaned the redwood-cased grandfather clock which had been passed from one generation to another for as long as he could remember. Every Saturday afternoon, he would clean, lubricate and polish the clock using a variety of oils and waxes. Each evening before going to bed he would make sure it was fully wound, and claimed it was this loving care which guaranteed its continued accuracy.

When Stephen died at the age of seventy-two, the old grandfather clock mysteriously stopped. It was the first time Molly had known it to stop ticking, and could not accustom herself to its deafening silence.

Over the following weeks, both family and friends tried to make it work, but could find nothing wrong. It was in an immaculate condition both inside and out, although the redwood case was no longer shining as it once did and now appeared dry, dull and misty. They could only conclude that it too had died, but it was an eerie sight because its hands were fixed at the exact time of Stephen's death, and no amount of gentle persuasion would move them.

A few weeks later, Molly's youngest daughter, Lori, came to visit. During their conversation, Molly mentioned the old grandfather clock, saying that she was not sure what to do about it. She had considered having it repaired, but that seemed sacrilegious. The clock had been so much a part of Stephen, and it was so appropriate for it to stop when he died, that having it repaired would be like bringing back the dead.

Lori, in her early thirties, reassured her mother, explaining there was no rush to make any decisions. If Molly felt so strongly about the clock being repaired, then she should forget all about it and enjoy the comfort she was then receiving from it.

On Stephen's death, the grandfather clock should have passed to the family's oldest son, but as there were no sons, it would automatically go to the oldest grandson. Unfortunately, there were no grandsons either. Lori's older sister had been married and divorced twice and was currently living with a man in Germany, with no children from any of the relationships. Lori herself had been married for some years but had no immediate plans to start a family.

Lori reasoned that the clock was legitimately owned by some future family male who did not exist at present. After all, there was no guarantee that Lori or her sister would have a son, and Molly could find herself having the old clock sacrilegiously repaired many times before a male child was old enough to take over the responsibility.

Molly agreed with her daughter. She was not sure who would be skilled in the repair of such an antique anyway, and it was far too valuable to let some back-street mechanic play around with it. Besides, she could feel Stephen's presence almost every time she went near the clock, an experience that was so strong, it was almost like Stephen was in the room with her, and she did not want to do anything to change *that*!

And so the grandfather clock remained, standing against the wall in the family room, quietly serene, watching and waiting as life went on around it; an ancient timepiece for which time did not exist. Molly dusted its case occasionally and tried to restore its former appearance, but she could never quite obtain the same shine that Stephen achieved when he used to lubricate and polish the clock each weekend.

About a year after Stephen's death, Molly arrived home with the weekend groceries, and her neighbour, Frank, who had kindly volunteered to help choose some paint for the outside of the house. Molly had barely entered when she stopped suddenly and turned to Frank in a panic. Frank asked what was wrong, then noticed too. The grandfather clock was now ticking.

Frank had collected Molly earlier in his car, and would have known if the clock was working then. Somehow, it had started while they were both out of the house, and when they entered the family room, they could see its hands had moved only ten minutes.

While they were trying to reason an explanation, the phone rang. It was Lori's husband phoning to tell Molly some good news. Lori had been taken to hospital earlier that morning, and had given birth to a son just fifteen minutes before. Molly was elated and rushed to tell Frank. He congratulated her and remarked how amazing life was that, while Lori was giving birth to Molly's first grandson, the two of them had been mundanely discussing painting the house on the way back from the supermarket. They both laughed. But then Frank suddenly stopped laughing and asked if Molly realised how much time had elapsed since the clock started working again. It was fifteen minutes! They instantly fell silent, the only sound in the entire house was the loud ticking from the old grandfather clock.

Two days later, Lori arrived with her husband and baby. As soon as she noticed the clock ticking, she remarked what a wonderful thought it was to have it repaired for their son's first visit with his grandmother.

Molly asked Lori if she felt strong enough for a shock, and proceeded to tell the couple she did not need to have the clock repaired, because it started working all by itself, apparently at the exact moment of the baby's birth.

Messenger From Beyond

This case is a rare one from a supernatural point of view, as well as being unusual in a medical sense, although it is by no means unique in either instance. One could hardly say this case was actually reported; it was, more accurately, 'discovered' seventeen years after the event by someone who had no connection other than by dating the granddaughter portrayed. I found it fascinating that the boyfriend never doubted the phenomena to be described, and instead he asked for an opinion about a purely medical aspect concerning the weight of his girlfriend at birth, assuming that point to be even more supernatural than the ghost itself.

I T WAS THE COLDEST February for many years, and snow lay thick upon the ground. If Edith Clegg had not promised her sister Vera that she would visit that day, there was no way she would have left her fireside on such a bleak afternoon. Edith had no telephone, and neither did her widowed sister, so there was nothing for it but to wrap up as warmly as possible and brave the elements.

She had left a hotpot in the oven, and as she pulled on her coat, she reminded her youngest daughter, Alma, to take it out around five o'clock. Her other daughter, Hilda, was relaxing by the fire with her feet up.

Hilda's husband was serving with the army in Germany, and hoped to be home in a few months. They had their own home, just a couple of avenues from Edith's house, but as Hilda had not been feeling too good, she was staying with Edith for a few days. Hilda was seven months pregnant with her first baby, which was due some time in April.

On that bitterly cold day, Edith set off, promising her daughters she would be home around ten o'clock. She had a long miserable wait for a bus. By the time it arrived, her feet and hands were numb with cold, and it was already pitch dark, though it was not yet four o'clock.

The long journey of forty kilometres to her sister's home seemed to take an eternity. At last, she stepped off the bus, and began the exhausting trek up the steep hill of terraced houses. Snow began to fall again, reducing visibility to a minimum. When Edith was just a few doors away from Vera's home, she stopped for a moment to catch her breath. As she stood there on the narrow, snow-covered pavement, frozen and weary, Edith felt as if she was the only living soul to be out on such a terrible afternoon.

She was about to go on, when she saw her mother near Vera's door. She stared hard through the swirling snow. She was not hallucinating, it was definitely her mother, standing there in the old woollen dress she so often used to wear and the inevitable apron around her plump waist. What troubled Edith was the fact that her mother had died many years before. A moment later the apparition was gone. Edith shook herself. The vision of her mother had disturbed her greatly.

Vera immediately opened the door to Edith's knock and helped her sister to take her coat off, suggesting that she take her boots off too, as Vera would find some slippers for her. The kettle was on, ready to make a welcomed pot of tea which Edith was in desperate need of. She was frozen to the marrow.

Edith sat on the chair in the hall to pull her boots off, while Vera rushed off to the kitchen to make the tea. Edith had said nothing to her sister about seeing their mother. She still did not know what to make of it.

Just as she was about to rise and go to join Vera in the kitchen, her mother suddenly appeared again before her. Here in the narrow hall, the woman was so clear to see, that Edith flopped back down on the chair with a startled gasp.

Her mother said not a word, but her expression was a worried one, and twice she raised her arm and pointed to the door as if indicating that Edith should depart Vera's house at once. Then, just as suddenly as before, she was gone.

Edith sat dazed for a short time; she had not even started to get the circulation going again in her frozen limbs. Slowly she pulled her boots back on, then her coat and hat. At that moment, Vera returned to the hall to see what was delaying her sister.

She asked Edith what on earth she was doing, putting on her coat and boots again. The tea was made and she had buttered some crumpets.

Edith shook her head, and simply stated that she had to get back home. She did not know why; it was something she just had to do.

Vera thought she was mad to go back out in the snow, without even a cup of tea inside her, and with no viable explanation for doing so. She was absolutely flabbergasted by her sister's irrational behaviour.

Edith left her sister immobile on the doorstep, staring after her in stunned surprise. It was a precarious descent to the bus stop. She was so cold and exhausted that it was impossible to think clearly. The only thing she was certain of was that her mother had appeared to her as a warning of some kind, and she had to get home as soon as she possibly could. Thankfully a bus arrived within twenty minutes. On a day like this when so many buses were not running, it was indeed a blessing.

When she reached her own street she covered the distance to her front door as quickly as she could. The very second she entered the house she knew her arrival was not a moment too soon.

Alma came running down the stairs, sobbing with relief at the sight of her mother. She told Edith she had run out a few minutes earlier, to phone for an ambulance. Hilda's baby was arriving; Alma was almost hysterical.

Edith threw off her coat and rushed upstairs. One look at her daughter was enough, and she knew instantly the ambulance would not be in time.

Through a haze of pain, Hilda managed a brave smile, it was obvious that there was not a moment in her life when she had been more grateful to see her mother.

Never before had Edith delivered a baby. But she suddenly felt her mother present in the room and knew then, that she would somehow manage. Edith sent Alma downstairs for hot water and towels, and prayed with all her might that her mother would guide her actions.

Within ten minutes, Hilda's daughter was safely delivered. The tiny infant could not have weighed more than a kilogramme, and looked in a critical condition.

Hilda was frantic. She was certain her tiny daughter would die at any moment. The baby was blue in places and made no movement whatsoever; she did not even cry.

But Edith reassured her. This baby was going to live, thanks to her mother.

Edith quickly filled a drawer from the dressing table with warm blankets and a hot water bottle, and laid the tiny infant in there. She knew that her mother, after all these years, had come through from the spirit realm to send her home so she could bring this fragile infant into the world, and Edith was certain that her miniature granddaughter, despite struggling for every breath, would survive.

At last they heard the siren of the ambulance. Their relief was immeasurable.

As Edith's granddaughter grew into a strong healthy baby during the next few months, there was barely a day went by when Edith failed to send out a thought of thanks to her dead mother. She did not dare contemplate what might have happened if she had not seen her ghost standing before her on that bleak February afternoon, compelling her to hurry home.

97

Young Lady Of Barton

It would be hard to find a case which involved so much discussion before it was reported. Word soon leaked out about the sighting, and some folks in the neighbourhood believed Hazel's story, while some did not. The situation was further complicated by confirmation from Hazel's friend, as this was taken as proof of a conspiracy. The Institute for Psychical Research was thought by a neighbour to be the best means of deciding the issue, and thereby the integrity of the two young girls. When the neighbour finally made the report, almost eight months after the sighting, investigators arrived at Hazel's home to be greeted by almost her entire family, who were there to make sure their wishes regarding another relative were obeyed, before any further information would be forthcoming. The wishes were reasonable but the demands were not. However, an amiable agreement was struck, and what started as a normal report, turned into a notably historic case.

BEING A COUNTRY girl at heart, Hazel relished every opportunity that came her way to visit her great-aunt Catherine's house in the quiet village of Barton, Lancashire. Catherine had no children of her own, and so Hazel was duly made a great fuss of.

At fourteen years old, Hazel was accustomed to visiting her great-aunt without her parents. It was not unusual, however, for Hazel to take along her school chum, Julie, for companionship. Julie always enjoyed these jaunts; there was so much for the two girls to see and do. And so it was, on a quiet Sunday afternoon, that the girls boarded a bus from their home town to visit Hazel's great-aunt Catherine.

Finishing their coffee and home-made scones, the teenagers set off to explore, full of the energetic excitement that comes naturally to girls of their age. They sauntered through Catherine's back garden, which sloped down to join the fields below. The garden was filled with fruit bushes and vegetables as well as a profusion of flowers. They stopped momentarily to pick a handful of peas, then ran playfully across the fields to the canal. Once there, they sat on its grassy bank, enjoying the tranquil scene. The warm sunlight reflecting off the water was hypnotic, making them both feel suddenly lazy.

After half an hour of school gossip, Hazel offered to show Julie around the old churchyard. Her friend made a derisive remark about this, but went along willingly enough. It took them about ten minutes to reach the churchyard which, like Catherine's garden, sloped down to the fields they were in.

They entered a section of the churchyard where most of the graves were old, and as they meandered along, Julie would stop occasionally to read an inscription. They were climbing steadily upward, and within a few minutes, had almost reached the church itself. On their left, were some mature laurel bushes.

Suddenly, Julie came to an abrupt halt, her eyes growing wide. She watched with fascination as a mass of white, smoke-like substance curled from the branches of a laurel bush and took on the form of a young woman, who stood just a short distance in front of Julie. She was wearing what seemed to be a thin, white nightdress. The neckline was high and its length ended at her calf, accentuating the fact that her slender feet were bare. Her long, golden hair shone brilliantly in the sunlight which appeared to cascade over every strand, only her parting in the middle hinting of shadow. Her expression was sad and preoccupied.

The whole sequence was enacted within a couple of minutes and had barely registered on Julie's mind, when the young ghost vanished. Julie's first reaction was to look over her shoulder to see where Hazel was. She saw that her friend was some distance behind her, bending over a tabletop grave as if she had been reading the inscription on it. But, from her conspicuous, startled expression, Julie knew that she too had seen the apparition.

Without any preamble, the two girls hurried from the churchyard and began their walk back to Catherine's house via the main road. During this short journey, they assimilated what they had seen. It was obvious to both of them that they had observed the exact same details of the young woman. Julie experienced amazement more than anything else and she was quick to realise that her friend was far more perturbed than she was. What neither of them could quite get over, was not so much the fact of having seen a ghost, but that they had seen one in broad daylight, with the scents of summer wafting around them on a warm, almost tropical breeze.

As they neared Catherine's house, Hazel gripped Julie's arm and pulled her to a halt. She wore a worried expression as she explained that her great-aunt had also seen, in all probability, the very same ghost. Apparently, Catherine had told Hazel of a peculiar sight which she frequently saw from her bedroom window.

Perhaps two or three times each week, Catherine would wake up during the early hours of the morning feeling restless and not at all sleepy. She always went to the bedroom window and gazed out at the darkened landscape. The curtains were never closed, as she liked to wake each morning to the newness of daybreak. There was therefore an immediate, unobstructed, though dimmed view of the fields below, of the canal and beyond. Within a minute of reaching the window, Catherine never failed to see the figure of a young girl wearing a calf-length, thin, white nightdress. There were numerous sightings under sufficient moonlight to be certain of the description. Even the long, golden hair was illuminated by the moon, and it could plainly be seen that, while appearing to walk, the apparition was in fact gliding at about thirty centimetres above the ground.

Catherine continued to watch in awe as the young woman crossed the field below. She would appear from behind the hedge on one side and walk through the field until she was hidden by a cluster of trees on the other side. Some nights she travelled in the opposite direction, but always wearing only a nightdress and gliding above the ground while her bare feet stepped as if in a walk.

Julie was already convinced that they had both seen a ghost in the churchyard, but now she was even more convinced, and somewhat relieved that at least one adult had seen the same young woman. She asked Hazel if she thought her aunt would tell them of any more experiences of the ghost.

Hazel looked horrified, exclaiming that they should not even contemplate asking her about ghosts. After all, there was no need. Catherine had told her about these particular experiences many times, and Hazel was sure it was the one and only ghost seen by her aunt. Every time she woke up in the early hours, she would go to the window and see the young woman in the field below. It was so consistent, it was almost an habitual occurrence on the part of both Catherine and the ghost.

So anxious was Hazel for Julie not to mention the ghost in front of Catherine, that she insisted on her pledge. Julie dutifully promised her friend, but protested that she could not see the reason for such a reaction. Surely Hazel's great-aunt would feel as relieved as Julie did, if she knew someone else had also seen the ghost.

Hazel explained that when her aunt told her about these strange sightings, not once did she describe the figure as a ghost. She seemed to think it was a vision of the night, almost like a dream one has, albeit awake at the time. It had never frightened her to see the figure. But they could not mention the matter in her presence, because Catherine did not realise what the vision actually was. And if she as much as suspected that she had in fact seen a ghost, it would terrify her.

The statement was a serious one, also echoed by Hazel's parents as well as other family members, and thus presented many difficulties for a thorough investigation of the case. Catherine was not in the best of health, but her sightings of the ghost still had to be authenticated if at all possible, while not at the expense of her well-being.

The Institute for Psychical Research, however, offers immeasurable astuteness in challenges such as this, and a carefully plotted strategy resulted in the conclusive confirmation of Catherine's sightings of the ghostly young lady of Barton, and a description of her movements, all without Catherine being aware that she had seen anything other than a vision of the night.

It proved invaluable testimony, for as closely as can be ascertained, Catherine saw the same ghost over two thousand times during a period of seventeen years, the highest frequency in any case history yet recorded.

The identity of the apparition remains unknown, but investigators confirmed her presence both in the churchyard and the field.

Catherine knew nothing of the investigation of this case and a guarantee of secrecy was afforded for the duration of her life. It has remained top secret until recently when, sadly, IPR were informed that Catherine had died.

It is with equal sadness that, without breaking the confidentiality by interviewing Catherine in greater depth, an important aspect of research was missed: it would have proved extremely interesting to discover whether Catherine awoke in anticipation of the ghost's walk, or if the ghost was actually responding to Catherine's insomnia. Alas, it remains a mystery how Catherine always saw the ghost each time she could not sleep, because there is no routine to the appearance of the ghostly young lady of Barton.

The Tag-Along Ghost

Hauntings can be as complex and varied as human nature itself. The details received for this case were both neat and concise, owing much to the percipient's character. If she had been of a less responsible nature, the information received may have been rather more scanty, thereby making the investigation and confirmation more difficult. But from the outset, Sue used logic and her powers of reasoning. Something was happening to her and she was not the sort to simply shrug it aside. The fact that Sue did not speak of her experiences with either her parents or friends at university, shows that she had the maturity to assess and evaluate for herself and was in no way self-seeking or looking for attention. When, at a later date, she sought help and advice from Jake, she did so with reticence. Naturally, Sue needed questions answered, and as the phenomena increased, becoming more insidious, Sue was afraid of being unable to handle the situation on her own.

S UE WAS IN A cheerful mood as she drove home from university on Friday afternoon. She was less than ten minutes from home when she noticed a young woman standing on the sidewalk intently watching the cars as they approached, giving the impression she was waiting for someone. She looked vaguely familiar to Sue, who thought she had seen her around the university campus.

Giving two light taps on the horn, Sue sharply pulled her black Trans Am to the side of the tree-lined avenue and stopped with the intention of asking the young woman if she needed a ride somewhere. But, as she glanced back in the rear-view mirror, there was no sight of her. Sue was non-plussed. Where could she have gone?

To be absolutely certain, Sue climbed out of the car, leaving the driver's door open as she walked a short distance back along the avenue. There was no sign of the young woman, so with a shrug of her shoulders, Sue returned to her car. She reviewed the strange event in her mind as she surveyed the immediate vicinity. Most of the homes in this area were detached houses built of block and wood, with generous gardens front and back. The scent of oleanders was heavy on the warm air. Suddenly, in the back of her mind, came a tiny, momentary spark of recognition. Then just as quickly it was gone, and Sue could do nothing more than to start the car and continue her journey home.

It was a beautiful, warm evening and Sue sat out on the patio at home as she ate a snack and worked on a project for one of her classes. She wanted to complete the work today so that the weekend would be free. The loud buzzing of the desert beetles was so familiar that she paid it no attention; nor the magnificent, panoramic view of the valley below, where scrub bushes and yucca trees peppered the oatmeal landscape.

She had the large, luxurious home to herself. Her father, a dentist, had flown out that afternoon for a dental convention and would not return until late on Sunday. Her mother, Lois, worked at the local hospital, and it would be hours yet before she arrived home.

Absorbed in her work, Sue lost track of time. The arid heat had given her a thirst and she decided to go inside for a glass of milk. Entering the large kitchen, Sue opened the refrigerator door, reached for a carton of milk, then suddenly tensed.

Someone had come into the room. Fear heightened her senses and caused a cold sticky sensation at the back of her skull. The sound was muted. A footstep or two. A vague shuffling sound. The wall clock showed it was not yet time for her mother to be home. Besides, she always called out a cheerful greeting, and would not come creeping into the kitchen.

Slowly, Sue turned to face the intruder, her mind numb, sluggishly trying to plan some means of defence.

When she saw there was no one there, Sue sighed with relief. She poured a glass of milk and sat at the breakfast bar to drink it, switching on the portable TV for company. Usually, Sue was not anxious about being alone in the house, and could not imagine what had caused her to react the way she had done a few minutes before: she would have sworn someone had come into the room. It was at this point that Sue recalled her drive home and stopping to offer a ride to the young woman who had so mysteriously vanished.

The sound of the front door announced her mother's arrival, followed by the usual, cheerful: 'I'm home, Honey. Everything okay?'

'Fine, Mom,' Sue replied, switching on the coffee machine. Now that her mother was home, she was less inclined to dwell upon either incident. However, throughout the evening, Sue found herself trying to recall the young woman's name. She was sure she recognised her from the university.

Sue stayed up late that evening to watch a movie. Snuggled close to her mother on the sofa, munching popcorn and doughnuts, Sue easily pushed aside her twinges of apprehension. Both incidents, after all, could surely be explained: the young woman could have gone into one of the houses; though she would have needed to really sprint to be out of sight within the time it took Sue to pull over and climb out of the car. As for the second occurrence, perhaps there had been some kind of minute subsidence in the foundations which caused the sounds in the kitchen. It was a weak theory. Nevertheless, Sue decided to stick to it for the time being, if only for peace of mind. Once in bed, Sue quickly fell asleep.

It was close to six o'clock the next morning when she awoke, and was about to roll over and try to resume her sleep. But the next instant, Sue recalled what had roused her at such an early hour: it was the voice, a plaintive, persistent, female voice, calling her name, over and over. It disturbed her, especially as Sue had never experienced anything like it before. However, she tried to dismiss the voice as a fragment of some weird dream. It was hardly an auspicious start to a day she had been looking forward to with anticipation. Greg, her boyfriend, would be coming over after lunch, and her mother had promised to take her shopping for some new clothes that morning, so with determination, Sue attempted to forget about her early morning experience.

It was a gloriously hot day. After a morning of shopping it was sheer bliss to sit out on the patio drinking ice-cold root beer and eating tuna fish salad. When the phone rang, Lois jumped up: 'It's probably your father, Honey. Sit and finish your salad.'

A couple of minutes later, Lois returned: 'A wrong number, I guess,' she told her daughter. 'I picked up the phone and there wasn't a darn thing, just a kinda static.'

Lois had just sat down when the phone rang again. Sue insisted on going this time. It was Greg, he was calling to say he would be over a little later than expected. They talked for a few minutes, then suddenly Greg was cut off in mid-sentence. The line had not gone dead. There was, as her mother had described, a sort of static interference.

Sue heaved a frustrated sigh and put the phone down. There were certainly some creepy things going on around here. But why pick on me, thought Sue.

As she joined Lois on the sun-drenched patio, Sue heard her mother laugh. 'Guess what, Honey. I swear this house of ours is haunted. I heard the patio door close a few minutes ago. Thought you were coming back out, but I could see through the window you were still on the phone.'

Lois had attempted to sound nonchalant, but Sue was not taken in. She had no wish to worry her mother, and although she made a joke about it, Sue toyed with her salad for which she no longer had an appetite.

That night, Sue awoke from a deep sleep. As she strove to keep her eyes open, she heard it again: not a voice this time, but a rapid knock-knock on her bedroom door. Just how long this had persisted, Sue was unsure. She lay rigid in her bed waiting for a repeat of the sound, but none came. It had been the kind of urgent knock one might use to wake someone without rousing the rest of the house.

Sue scrambled from her bed, threw on her robe and hurried to the kitchen, where she made a cup of hot chocolate, then snuggled on the sofa. She had no desire to return to her bedroom. It would have been a comfort to have shared her mother's room, though the only excuse Sue could think of was that she had woken from a nightmare, and she had not troubled her parents with that sort of thing since kindergarten. So Sue resigned herself to spend the rest of the night in the living room.

Sunday was a pleasant day. Sue helped her mother clean out the garage, then drove over to Greg's house for a couple of hours. When her father arrived home, he took Sue and Lois out to dinner. Not a single creepy happening had occurred all day. And to Sue's relief, she was not woken that night.

As Sue drove to the university the next day, she had managed to put aside the disturbing incidents.

During the lunch break, she was walking along one of the corridors when she noticed her friend, Tory, crossing the main hall. Sue called out to her. Tory stopped, and smiled as Sue approached, then looked, for a moment, a little perplexed. 'Something wrong?' Sue asked. Her friend was still staring at the corridor Sue had just come from.

'Who was that you were with?' Tory asked.

Sue frowned, and said she had not been with anyone.

Tory shook her head impatiently and explained that she had seen a girl walking to one side and slightly behind Sue. The girl looked familiar, yet Tory could not think who she was. Surely Sue must have seen her. Sue assured Tory that she had not, but it left her with an uncomfortable feeling. Tory too, for she was staring directly at the girl when she simply was not there anymore!

Perhaps, thought Sue, the girl had gone into one of the rooms off the corridor. But why had she not sensed someone behind her, or heard footsteps? It seemed that this was another strange incident to add to the rest. And she was now getting pretty darned tired of it all.

The moment she was through with classes that afternoon, Sue hurried over to Jake Linder's room. He had finished with his students but was talking with a colleague. The very instant they parted, Sue asked diffidently if she could talk with him. With his customary warmth and charm, Jake suggested they grab a drink and talk outside. They sat on a low wall in the sunshine. Jake had given lectures on the paranormal, so Sue reasoned he was the best person to approach. Besides, he was such a nice guy, so full of natural confidence and spontaneous concern for his students that if anyone could put her mind at rest, she knew he could.

She was soon pouring out her experiences to him, starting with when she stopped the car on Friday afternoon to offer a ride to the young woman who she thought might be a fellow student. Then she described the incident of feeling someone had come into the kitchen as she opened the refrigerator door; next, waking up because someone had been calling her name; then the static on the phone and her mother hearing the patio door close, when in fact it was already shut. The final two incidents had been the knock-knock on the bedroom door which had woken her, and Tory actually seeing a young woman in the corridor behind her, even though Sue was certain she was alone at the time.

Jake listened attentively, asking only an occasional question. He suggested that Sue should write down all she had experienced in as much detail as she could possibly recall, and get the notes to him the next day. Sue promised to do this. Already she felt a sense of relief from having talked to someone about it, and, hopefully, Jake would be able to give her an explanation about it all.

Sue handed over her notes the next morning, and Jake asked her to keep a journal of anything else that happened. What she had experienced so far had been enough to set her nerves on edge, but she registered instantaneous shock at Jake's request before realising fractionally later, that the ghost would not go away simply when Sue handed in her notes. Jake gave her his home phone number and told her to call if necessary, meanwhile she was to leave things with him for a couple of days.

The week progressed without any further incidents. On Thursday evening, however, as Sue was placing some recently processed photographs in her album, she came across one which made her catch her breath. It was a photograph she had taken of Jamie, one of her friends at the university. It was of Jamie's birthday party on the campus. The photo showed Jamie and Tory sitting opposite each other at a table they had taken outside. On the table stood the huge chocolate cake which Sue had made specially for the occasion. Both girls were hysterical with laughter, but what caught Sue's attention was the fact that in the background, inadvertently captured on film, was another student. The expression on this girl's face was one of absorbtion, as if, glancing round as she passed by, she had been drawn to the happy scene, of which she took no part.

It all clicked into place now. This girl with the forlorn look was the same young woman Sue had seen standing on the sidewalk last Friday. It was the way she appeared, so lost and helpless, which had encouraged Sue to pull over to ask if she needed a ride.

Sue now recalled further details. The girl's name was Babs. She attended the university for only a short time, two months at the most, and was in some of the same classes as Sue, Tory and Jamie. As far as Sue could remember, Babs had arrived because her father was relocated in his work. No one had really taken to her, but Sue had sometimes made an effort to talk to Babs and sit with her for lunch. Sue also remembered now, seeing Babs waiting for the bus, and stopping to give her a ride to university. This had probably occurred only twice, and she recalled giving her a ride home on one occasion. Babs was the kind of unnoticed teenager who did not make friends easily. When she died suddenly due to a brain haemorrhage, sadly no one had really missed her.

It was a little late in the day to feel sympathy for the girl, as she must have been dead for almost four months. Sue could not recall seeing her more than once after Jamie's birthday. In fact, she would never have remembered the girl at all, but for the photograph. Only now did Sue realise that Babs had lived in one of those houses near to where she stopped last Friday to offer her a ride.

Sue decided to show the photograph to Jake the next day and pulled it from the album. Also, she would ask Tory if this was the same girl she had seen behind her in the corridor. She put the photograph in her purse so there was no chance of forgetting it.

Only after classes had finished the next day did Sue have an opportunity to see Jake. She recounted to him everything she had remembered, while she searched her purse for the photograph. It was not to be found, despite emptying the contents on the floor and shaking her diary and address book in case it had got stuck inside one of them.

Sue could not understand it. She was positive about putting it in her purse the night before. Jake smiled enigmatically and told her not to worry. At least they had a name now, and he would see what he could learn from the university's records. What Sue could not understand was why Babs had chosen to haunt *her*!

Jake suggested that perhaps Babs was drawn to Sue because of the effort she had made to befriend her. Also, as Babs did not appear to be an outgoing person, possibly Sue represented the type of young woman Babs wished she could have been. After all, Sue was content with her life, was a straight-A student, had loving parents, and was popular with everyone.

As Sue drove home that afternoon, passing as she always did, the avenue where Babs once lived, she wondered if any of this would ever have started had she not 'seen' Babs standing on the sidewalk and had not stopped, but gone straight home; she thought of her action now as giving an open invitation for the ghostly Babs to come home with her, and had been followed intermittently ever since. The more Sue thought about it, there was probably no better invitation to be haunted, than stopping to offer a ride to a ghost.

Since Monday, however, Sue had been left in peace, and she hoped things would stay that way. In time, she might be able to forget about Babs.

On Sunday morning, Sue helped her mother with the laundry, taking towels from the bathrooms and stripping sheets from the beds. She was about to enter her own bedroom to do the same, when she froze in her tracks. Her bedroom door was open, giving Sue a clear view of none other than Babs, sitting at the dressing table! ·

Sue dropped the laundry she was carrying and ran to the kitchen. Sitting at the breakfast bar, she could see her mother outside cutting some flowers. It made her feel safe, and she had no wish to worry her mother by running screaming from the house.

Gradually, Sue calmed down and allowed herself to think about what she had seen a few minutes before. It had all happened so quickly, but every minute detail had been absorbed: the opened bedroom window; the ruffled sheets of her bed; the opened closet door; everything just as she left it before breakfast. Except, there, at her dressing table, was Babs, sitting there as if it was the most natural thing in the world. What had also struck fear into Sue's heart, was the atmosphere of the room. The air was still; the echo of her own personality, somehow extracted. It was a beautiful sunny morning, with a warm wind blowing. When she had opened her window on getting out of bed, the wind had blown the lacy drapes with ease and filled the room with the scent of desert flowers. However, in that bizarre instance of looking into her room, the drapes did not blow about on the warm wind. They were still. Nor did the room smell of desert blooms. Instead, there had been a cloying scent of stale chrysanthemums: a definite stench of decay clung to the air. Not only this, but there was also a fuzzy density to the very air itself, making the room appear out of focus, colours washed out, muted.

Sue shuddered. It took a supreme effort, but she forced herself to go back to her room. She held her breath as she stood at the doorway. But there was nothing to fear now. The room was exactly as it should have been, warm, fresh, full of sunshine, the air clear, the drapes blowing about merrily.

However, Sue knew that she could never use this room again. With speed and determination, she moved all her belongings to one of the guest bedrooms at the other side of the house. It was not as pretty as her own room, and she felt a deep resentment. The whole thing had been a kind of violation. Nothing and no one had caused her such distress before.

During lunch, Sue mentioned to her mother that she had switched rooms, and made up an excuse for having done so. It would have been a relief to have confided in her parents, but it was something she could not bring herself to do.

That afternoon, Sue drove over to Greg's house as arranged. As she parked her car in front of the magnificent house, Sue felt an immense relief. She had escaped, if only for a short while, and she aimed to make the most of it.

At university the next day, Sue's friend Tory, made a derisory remark about Sue's perfume. She did not mean to be rude, but it really was ghastly, and she suggested that Sue should wash it off. Sue explained that she was not wearing any perfume. Tory said she had got to be kidding! It was like rotting vegetation. Or, something! The other girls screeched with laughter, and teased Sue about it for the rest of the day. Sue could smell nothing herself. When she had been a little girl her mother had often remarked that she had a Daddy-smell, after Sue had been cuddling on her father's knee and the scent of his aftershave had rubbed off on her. But surely the stench of decay she had noticed in her room, and now associated with the ghost of Babs, could not have rubbed off on her. The very thought made Sue feel sick, and she hardly knew how she managed to get through the rest of the day at the university.

As she hurried to her car later that afternoon, she bumped into Jake. Almost angrily, she filled him in on the latest events. This could not continue, she told him, her whole life was being messed up and, it was about time Jake offered some real help, other than requesting she keep her journal up to date. Jake nodded his head in agreement, as he could understand Sue's aggression. He promised her he would call a friend of his that evening, who he was sure would be able to offer some positive assistance.

Later that year, as the first week of the fall semester progressed, no one would have suspected that three months previously Sue had suffered the most harrowing experience of her young life. Now, as she hurried through the university, her only concern, and an extremely minor one at that, was that she was going to be a little late for her English class. She was bright and cheerful, full of energy and seemed not to have a care in the world. As indeed she did not. The ghost of Babs, like an unwanted guest, had been swiftly expelled from her home on the evening Jake had summoned his friend to her aid. The young man had arrived with four other investigators from The Institute for Psychical Research, and done their stuff, as Sue thought of it. It had worked out beautifully, as her folks had gone out that evening to have dinner with friends. It had been like a blessing, a miracle. Sue still had IPR's card in her purse, and had been told to call if ever she felt the need. But thankfully, she had never needed to. There had been no scandal, no necessity to worry her parents, and no continuous quips from her friends; fortunately, Jake was the only person at university to know about the haunting.

Although, more out of superstition and not wanting to tempt fate, Sue had not yet returned to her former bedroom, she felt pretty sure that if she did, all would be well, as she had never seen the melancholy Babs from that evening to this day, months later. And day by day, the memory of it all had become more faded. It was past, done with, over!

That afternoon, as Sue walked across the campus with her friend Tory to where their cars were parked, Tory stopped unexpectedly and grasped Sue's arm as if suddenly having remembered something important she had intended to convey to Sue.

Tory's eyes were wide with gleeful anticipation as she told Sue that on her way home the day before, she had noticed a young woman standing on the sidewalk as if needing a ride. Tory felt that the girl was vaguely familiar and thought she had seen her around the university. Anyway, she had pulled over to offer a ride, but the girl had vanished into thin air! Which as far as Tory was concerned was a really peculiar thing to have happened.

Sue felt her blood run cold. She fumbled in her purse and, finding the card with IPR's phone number on it, pushed it forcefully into Tory's hand. 'Call them!' she demanded, then leaving Tory standing there looking non-plussed, Sue ran to her car and took a different route home: only a fool would tempt fate.

A Haunting Holiday

Although this occurrence may seem varied, the case stands apart by virtue of its consistency. Anyone meeting the ghost's idealistic standards was left, literally, in peace; whereas, anyone who had the misfortune not to meet with approval was made exceedingly uncomfortable. Some people may think that this particular case is a haunting of the worst kind, and may even consider it to be a malicious or evil entity. This, however, is not so. Simply because someone has passed from this world, does not mean that their emotive responses are null and void, as this case by itself indicates. It was, in essence, the ghost's prerogative to cause a disturbance. It came to our attention through the electrician portrayed, whose sole interest, it seems, did not concern the ghost's identity or even the reason for the haunting. What he wanted to know was how an electrical fault caused by this kind of occurrence, should be remedied. Even more amazing, it was the first time such a request had ever been made to us by someone outside our faculty.

R UTH AND EMILY appeared to have much in common. Each of the widowed sisters lived alone in bungalows on the outskirts of Folkestone, Kent. They shared the same interest and veneration in the distinguished history of Folkestone, and both dearly loved their regular walks through the old and new towns. Even their physical similarities caused them frequently to be mistaken for twins.

On closer inspection, however, the two sisters were as different, in many respects, as chalk and cheese.

Despite their sisterly love for each other and their closeness in years, they pursued totally individual lives. Ruth lived on the east side of the popular holiday resort, while Emily lived on the west side. Although they often visited the same museum, they did so on separate days, as if by arrangement, even though no such agreement was ever made. Ruth walked around Folkestone in a clockwise direction early in the morning, starting from the picturesque Old

Town near the harbour and including the attractive scenery afforded by the rosemary bushes along the Road of Remembrance and the impressive Victorian terraces of The Leas. She would return by way of Bouverie Road and cutting through to the parish church of St Mary and Eanswith, before completing the tour at the end of The Old High Street.

While Ruth taught the piano at home in the afternoon, Emily would be taking her afternoon walk, which started from The Leas and included the same magnificent splendour along the same route that her sister walked, except that it was taken in an anticlockwise direction.

Housework to Ruth was a chore to be done as quickly as possible so she could get on with living. All of her neighbours must have trampled through her bungalow at one time or another for piano lessons, coffee, or a chat. Emily, on the other hand, loved housework. She was as proud of her home as she was of living in the vicinity of such an ancient and historically important town as Folkestone. Her bungalow was her castle and if Emily did not approve of someone being in her home, they were certainly made aware of the fact.

The two sisters' minds were so much in tune with each other that there was only one subject on which they could not agree. Emily believed in ghosts, while Ruth did not. Emily often told her sister that she would one day change her opinion, and believe in ghosts. Ruth insisted she never would. Emily said it was inevitable. And this was how the conflict progressed whenever the subject was raised.

Ruth did change her opinion, however, but it was many years later, and only after some considerable expense.

It all started with Emily's death. Ruth was the only living relative and therefore inherited Emily's bungalow on the west side of Folkestone. There was no immediate necessity for Ruth to sell the property and so it remained empty for several months before she finally decided to rent it out as a holiday home. It proved a lucrative venture and was soon booked months ahead by holidaymakers.

Everything went smoothly in the beginning. A cleaner had been employed to maintain the bungalow and the first four families to stay there were highly satisfied.

The peak of the holiday season was just approaching when the initial hints of a hidden problem came to light. The first family to bring the matter to Ruth's attention seemed to have a tremendous struggle trying to gain access to the bungalow. It was their third day there, and they had just returned from sightseeing to find the front door would not open. They immediately phoned Ruth, who drove across town with her spare key, only to discover that the door opened with ease. The second occasion made her wonder how two adults could possibly fail to open the door when it opened so easily for her. On the third day of driving across town to help the family to gain access, Ruth was somewhat annoyed and did not even take her own key as she knew there was nothing wrong with the key the holidaymakers had. Each time there was nothing to indicate why the door would not open for the renting family, while it opened as if on well-oiled hinges for Ruth, despite her advancing years.

Ruth thought her prayers had been answered when the family's last few days passed without incident. She was a little surprised that they did not book next year's holiday as the other families had done, but was not too upset by it, given the trouble she had been put to.

What Ruth did not realise at the time was that the family did continue to have trouble opening the front door, and only avoided the necessity of phoning Ruth because they started leaving a window open every time they went out.

The next six weeks assured Ruth that no one else had difficulty gaining entrance to the bungalow. She even asked one young couple whether the door proved troublesome to open at all. The look on their faces was enough of an answer, and Ruth left feeling as though she had made a fool of herself.

Bookings had poured in, so there would be one family after another visiting throughout the high season. The last thing Ruth needed at this time, was an electrical problem in her sister's bungalow. But halfway through the week, the cooker failed to work.

A repair man was sent for, but could not find any fault in either the cooker or the wiring. There was obviously an intermittent fault, as the cooker seemed to work perfectly for the repair man, though, he puzzled, only when the wife of the renting family was not in the kitchen. It was decided that another cooker might be the easiest solution, so one was quickly bought, delivered and installed. However, the replacement cooker would not work at all, even though it seemed to be in perfect working order.

Connecting the original cooker again, the only answer seemed to lie in rewiring the kitchen, and just at this point, the television also developed an intermittent fault. Another repair man came, tested the television and in view of the cooker's defiance, concluded that the lounge too needed rewiring.

On hearing about the television, the first repair man suggested rewiring the whole bungalow, but Ruth wanted the work kept to a minimum; there had already been enough inconvenience to the renters. And while Ruth organised an electrician to rewire the kitchen and lounge, the family complained that the lights in the lounge and bedrooms were not working, and Ruth was forced to arrange for the whole bungalow to be rewired.

Before the work could commence, the family finished their week and left with a full refund and Ruth's apology for the inconvenience.

The next family were greeted by Ruth's explanation of the

electrical fault and offer to arrange alternative accommodation for their stay, while the rewiring was being done. They sympathised with Ruth and explained that they had no objection to staying in the bungalow while the work was going on, provided there was no major upheaval involved.

Ruth was relieved by their attitude, especially after the previous family's continual nagging about discomfort, lack of privacy (the repair men trying to correct the electrical problems), and their ruined holiday, as if Ruth had arranged the electrical failures herself.

Two days into their holiday, the husband of the current family phoned Ruth to tell her they had not experienced one problem with the lights, cooker or television. Ruth phoned the electrician to ask his advice, and, ultimately, it was decided to postpone the rewiring for the time being, as everyone agreed there was evidently nothing wrong with the wiring anyway.

The family's week ended without any electrical failure whatsoever. In spite of Ruth warning the next three families of possible rewiring work to correct the electrical problems, and assuring them of full reimbursement for any inconvenience caused, not one failure was reported.

By the end of the season, Ruth did not know what to do about the wiring. Only one family had been affected by the strange electrical failures, just as only one family had not been able to open the front door. The electrician suggested a thorough examination of the wiring now that the bungalow was empty, as he could not see any reason for the failures and the present wiring was no more than a few years old. He reported back the following day with virtually the same words. He told Ruth that it must have been a problem with the supply and not to worry about it, adding that she should phone him if there were any further problems.

A less subtle hint befell Ruth when she called in the decorator to Emily's bungalow. She knew the wallpaper was not what Emily would have chosen, but it was strong and durable, and much easier to maintain than the present homely cottage wallpaper.

When Ruth went to inspect the finished work, she was appalled by the sight of every strip of wallpaper lying complete, but crumpled on the floor. She immediately phoned the decorator to complain. He was at a total loss for an explanation, nevertheless he apologised and assured her that he would put the matter right.

A week later, he repapered throughout with diligence, but the wallpaper mysteriously came off the walls again, even though he had used the strongest adhesive available. By now he was less apologetic and would have been convinced that he was the subject of some hoax but for him knowing Ruth reasonably well, having regularly decorated her own bungalow.

Ruth recalled how Emily always decorated the entire bungalow by herself and without the slightest trouble. But Emily was no longer alive to tell her secret and all they could think of as a solution, was to choose a different, lighter wallpaper instead.

The decorator brought several pattern books into the lounge from his van for Ruth to look through. Only one pattern stuck in her mind: a cottage wallpaper that Emily would have loved, though its durability left much to be desired. However, nothing else seemed suitable and so Ruth finally relented to the impracticality and chose it.

The wallpaper was promptly ordered and smoothed on the walls, with the decorator remarking about Ruth considering painted walls if this wallpaper came down as well. Ruth was by now suspecting the connection with her sister because she was not altogether surprised that the new wallpaper stuck fast to the walls. Once the garden had been tidied, the bungalow was again ready for the next holidaying families.

An early spring booking started off the year with no end of problems. The family spent most of their week inside the bungalow and were pestered by the external doors and windows mysteriously opening by themselves. Every morning they awoke to find both doors and every window wide open, even though they were closed and locked the night before. Within an hour of them waking up each morning, the burglar alarm would also spring into life.

This proved puzzling as the alarm was switched off and Ruth was the only person with a key. If by some impossible means it had been switched on, it certainly did not account for it being triggered by the family waking up, rather than by the doors and windows being opened, which apparently happened shortly after the family retired for the night.

Then there were the same old problems with the cooker and television. The electrician told Ruth that the only conclusion he could arrive at, as there was nothing electrically wrong, was that the bungalow did not appear to like the family staying there. He said it in a joking manner, but Ruth found herself agreeing, not just with the electrician's comment, but with the opinion of the bungalow too. Every morning when she went to take care of the burglar alarm, she had to switch it on, then off, to stop its ringing, and each time, she found herself wanting to open the windows and doors, as the family were heavy smokers of some tobacco with a horrible smell, so that walking into the bungalow was like walking into an opium den.

Ruth no longer believed it was the bungalow causing these bizarre problems. She was now convinced that Emily was the one responsible. There seemed to be a systematic disapproval of certain families who, for one reason or another, upset Emily. And true to form, Emily made sure that her opposition was noted.

To confirm this belief, not one further problem was reported until late autumn when a middle-aged businessman and his lady friend arrived. He was in Folkestone on business and introduced the young lady as his personal assistant, not as his wife.

Ruth noticed that both of them wore wedding rings, which worried her a little as she was quite old-fashioned in that respect. Nevertheless, it was a delicate subject to broach at this late stage and she would have to assume they would be sleeping in separate bedrooms. After all, there was sufficient space in the bungalow to accommodate three couples.

The first night of their stay was enough to set the burglar alarm off. They had not been in bed five minutes when the loud shrill got them out again.

It was one o'clock in the morning when Ruth arrived. The businessman was fully dressed because of his journey to the nearest telephone kiosk, while his 'personal assistant' lounged on the couch in her dressing gown. The businessman explained that they had only just gone to bed when the alarm sounded, and Ruth was in no doubt why. This was confirmed by her going about the bungalow checking that all the windows were closed: only the bed in the master bedroom had been disturbed.

Ruth informed them that there must be a fault in the switch and diplomatically suggested they should both go to their separate bedrooms and she would stay for a few minutes in case the alarm sounded again.

The couple did as instructed, though they were obviously not overjoyed at the prospect of sleeping apart. Ruth waited for a short time before quietly closing the front door behind her. She sat in her car outside for twenty minutes, just to make sure it was going to remain quiet, before driving across town to her own bed.

At eight o'clock the following day, Ruth was again called out to stop the burglar alarm ringing. She realised this could not go on, no matter how much she and Emily disapproved of the couple sleeping in the same bed. They seemed quite insistent on being together and Ruth was forced to have the alarm completely disconnected.

On the couple's last day, Ruth asked if everything had been alright. They told her it had, although the alarm still went off every night and several times each day, but it sounded as though someone was cranking it by hand which was not really loud enough to disturb them. When they said they had enjoyed their holiday, Ruth was more than a little embarrassed and this had nothing to do with the fact that the couple were supposed to be on a business trip.

Next came a young couple who were booked for a stay of two weeks. Ruth assumed that they were a married couple, but was prepared for Emily's judgement.

The first night was quiet, as was the second: and Ruth breathed a

116

sigh of relief at the prospect of enjoying two weeks of normality. When her phone rang just after nine o'clock on the fourth evening of the young couple's stay, Ruth was surprised that it was to report another problem at the bungalow. There had been a power failure and the couple could not find the fusebox in the dark. Ruth routinely told the young man to expect her in about thirty minutes, and went to look for her torch.

She was about to leave, when the phone rang again. It was the husband informing her that the electricity must have come back on while they were at the telephone kiosk, as they found that the lights were on when they returned to the bungalow. Ruth asked if they still wanted her to take a look at the fuses, but they said they would be turning in for the night shortly, so it was agreed for Ruth to check on the fuses the following morning.

Ruth arrived as the couple were about to set off for a day trip. They left with Ruth's assurance to rectify any fault with the fuses. But she had not realised until then that the bungalow was actually fitted with circuit breakers rather than fuses, which Ruth decided were too complex for her to tamper with in looking for a faulty connection. She examined what she could, but everything seemed to be in order. Leaving a note for the couple, saying everything looked alright, she returned to her home wondering how such a nice young couple could possibly have upset Emily.

All was quiet again until about a week later when, once more, the electricity failed in Emily's bungalow. On this occasion it was during the afternoon and may not have been noticed but for the television being on at the time. Ruth thought the young man sounded very irritated on the phone and thought it best to ask the electrician to take a look.

He was waiting in front of the bungalow when she arrived. As soon as they entered, they could feel a tension in the air. The wife immediately went into the rear garden without a word and the husband seemed a little hostile as Ruth and the electrician made their way to the circuit breakers. They breathed a simultaneous sigh of relief when the husband too, left them alone.

Ruth expressed her concern about the electrical problems getting out of hand, causing an atmosphere like this. But the electrician told her that the atmosphere was nothing to do with the electrics; when he arrived he had approached the front door, and was about to knock, but heard the couple in the midst of a heated argument. He thought better of it and made a stealthy retreat to wait for Ruth.

Apparently, the husband had promised a trip to Canterbury that day, but then discovered there was a programme on TV that he preferred to watch. The wife was naturally upset about his broken promise. And it would seem Emily 'intervened' when the argument started.

The electrician used every trick he could think of to locate the fault, without success, although he did detect it was not a complete power failure after all. In fact, everything worked perfectly, except the one circuit from the mains to the television, no matter where it was plugged in. He was considerably worried about this, and muttered several times to himself that it was impossible.

Neither of them felt particularly inclined, under the circumstances, to go in search of the young couple, and so remained there, talking casually together.

After a while, the couple came in from the garden and announced they were going to Dover for the day. They had obviously made amends as they were now holding hands. The electrician was just telling them he had isolated the fault, but could not trace the cause, when the television suddenly came on. There was another tense moment before the husband tugged at his wife and the young couple strolled arm in arm out of the bungalow, leaving Ruth and the electrician spellbound and speechless.

The following summer brought displeasure for the next family to stay in the bungalow. In spite of the strict rule that no pets were allowed, the family had disregarded this and brought their small dog. Ruth did not suspect anything, as the family kept the dog hidden in the car when they arrived. They had not reckoned on Emily's watchful eye.

After unpacking, the family left the dog in the bungalow while they went out for a meal and to explore the area. When they returned at about ten o'clock, they were shocked to discover the dog had disappeared. They searched the bungalow thoroughly, but there was neither sight nor sound of the animal. All the windows and doors were closed, so they could not understand how their dog had managed to get out. The family continued their search outside, however, and by eleven o'clock, had found the dog nestling under a hedge nearby. Returning to the bungalow, they were annoyed to find the door would not open, and had to hide the dog in the car again while Ruth came down to let them in.

Ruth only needed to put the key in the lock and turn it, and the door opened without difficulty. Resigned to another troublesome week, Ruth drove home.

The husband then went out to the car to bring the dog inside. He had just stepped onto the front doorstep with the dog in his arms when the door slammed shut almost in his face, and no amount of effort by himself, or his family inside, could open it. Nor would the rear door open. It was perhaps fortunate for them that only the husband and the dog were outside, as the wife was able to open a window for them to climb through.

The following morning, they awoke to find the dog missing again. The doors now opened easily, but not taking any chances, the wife stayed inside while the husband and two children went in search of their pet.

Again, the doors were jammed closed on their return and they all had to climb in through the window. They were discussing whether or not to complain to Ruth about the doors when one of the boys announced that both the front and rear doors were open and he had just managed to stop the dog from escaping once more.

To add more confusion to the issue, shortly after either the front or rear door was closed, it would open again by itself. The husband examined the catches but could find nothing wrong, yet the doors would not stay closed for more than a few minutes.

Thus their week progressed. Whenever the dog was inside the bungalow, the doors would keep opening by themselves. When the dog had been outside then brought back, the doors would not open. The family always had to leave someone inside to let them in on their return. They tried letting the dog out in the rear garden and holding the door open, but when the dog's name was called, the door would tear from the grasp which held it and slam shut with a vengeance — or it would remain open as the dog bolted once more.

At night, the couple tried putting the dog in the second bedroom with the children, but no matter how firmly they wedged the bedroom door closed, it would open again and the dog would escape from the bungalow. It did not take them long to realise that the only way they could ensure the security of the bungalow while they slept, was to lock their dog in the car overnight.

Though Ruth received no further complaints, she suspected something was amiss when she inspected the bungalow after the family's departure. There was an abundance of conspicuous dog hairs on the furniture and carpets which were not there when the family had arrived, and Ruth found herself apologising to her deceased sister Emily who never allowed dogs in her home when she was alive. At the same time, Ruth knew that Emily would have let her wrath be known.

Final Farewell

What makes itself apparent in this case, is the desire, and the single-minded determination on the part of the ghost, to fulfil a purpose. The fact that such an aim was formed in an almost jocular manner, yet was honoured many years later, says much for the bond of love between one human being and another. A few days after the event, it was reported to us by a member of the family, for one reason and one alone: as a form of acknowledgement, to have official record and confirmation of one man's unquestionable dedication to his family, a quality so special, it would have been an insult to have left the event untold.

NEIL ROGERS (PSEUDONYM) was reasonably pleased with life that warm spring morning as he looked out of his office window at the lush, tropical vegetation of Balboa Park below. It was a refreshing break to see such a green and inviting scene amongst the buildings of the city centre. Not that the centre of San Diego, California, was displeasing to the eye; on the contrary, it was quaint, peaceful, and almost village-like, and Neil was especially poetic about beauty at that time, being quite ecstatic about his forthcoming wedding in ten days' time.

Neil, then in his early thirties, felt that there was not a single aspect about his life which he would change. He enjoyed his work as a lawyer, and got along well with his partner. Soon he would be marrying a young woman with whom he had grown up. He had no financial worries; his health and his prospects were excellent. Only one thing troubled this young man, namely, his father. Alan Rogers (pseudonym) was in his late sixties, and his health was a worry to both his wife and his son.

Neil arrived home a little earlier than usual that evening. The day had gone very smoothly. As he entered his parents' house, it was immediately apparent that something was amiss. There was no customary greeting from his father, which usually occurred upon entry, and as Neil looked into the living room, the television was not on, nor was his father sitting in his favourite easy chair, by the fireplace; nor was his mother in the kitchen, and there was no appetising smell permeating the air. Neil was worried. He had never before come home to an empty house; usually both his parents would be at home.

After making himself a coffee, Neil entered the living room to watch the news on television, yet alert for the sound of his parents' car pulling into the driveway.

Thirty minutes later, he sprang from his chair and rushed to the door. As his mother climbed out of the car, he hurried to her, asking where his father was.

Annie took her son's arm and as they entered the house she told him about another heart attack that afternoon and that Alan had been rushed into hospital. She quickly reassured her son that, all being well, Alan would be home in a day or two; he was fortunate in that the attack had been a mild one.

Neil went to visit his father the next day, and was relieved to find him sitting up in bed. He looked tired and pale, but his blue eyes had the same familiar glint of warmth and humour in them.

They were soon talking together as if nothing had happened, but it was obvious to Alan that something was troubling his son, and in his usual forthright manner asked what it was, assuring his son that there was no reason why his wedding should not go ahead as planned, as he had every intention of being there.

Neil shook his head, and carefully explained to his father that his worry was of a much deeper nature. The two of them were very close and Neil was shaken in that, while he was going about his day as usual without a care in the world, he had not the slightest indication that his father had collapsed and been taken to hospital. He questioned why he had not somehow sensed that something was wrong and that he was needed at home.

Alan brushed this aside. Annie had handled everything well enough, he reasoned, and though he felt quite weak, he would be home the following day, so it was not as if it had been a life or death situation. Alan could see his son was not satisfied with this response.

Neil said that his father might just as easily have died through a more severe attack and at, God forbid, the very moment he was looking out on the park from his office window and thinking what a wonderful day it was. He would never have been able to condone himself and it disturbed him greatly, especially as he would not have had even the opportunity to say goodbye.

To Neil's surprise his father laughed, and told his son that he need not worry; when the time came for him to die, he would make sure he said a last goodbye to Neil. Besides, he had no intention of leaving this earthly life just yet, not until he had at least seen his first grandchild.

The years passed by, and the day Neil had visited his father in the hospital as well as the talk they had, soon became a distant memory.

121

When Neil and his wife had been married for seven years they had a daughter, Katie, after virtually giving up hope of ever having a child.

Everyone thought the world of little Katie. From the moment she could walk, Alan loved to take her into his garden and let her help him pick tomatoes. The child adored her grandfather, and it was rare that a weekend went by without Neil and his wife taking her to Neil's parents' home.

When Katie was six years old, Neil and his wife were thrilled to discover that another child was on the way. One weekend, while at his parents' home, Neil told them the good news. His father asked when the baby was due, and Neil said that his wife had been given a date around the beginning of October. He was perhaps the only one to notice that while his father was obviously pleased, he also seemed pensive and distracted.

A little later, Alan took his granddaughter into the garden, and while Neil's mother and his wife were preparing a meal, Neil slipped quietly outside to join his father and daughter.

They were at the far end of the garden away from the house. On one side of the lawn lay a small square of earth which Alan had prepared some years before for Katie to have as her own little corner, in which to plant whatever she wished. Katie was proud of her little garden and had grown mint and strawberries as well as some flowers, with just a little help from her grandfather.

As Neil approached, as yet unobserved, he saw that his father was digging a similar miniature garden on the other side of the lawn. He heard Alan tell Katie that this was for her brother, when he was old enough. Katie was to help the little guy to grow things, and whenever he got the chance he would visit Katie and her brother, and watch them at work in their little gardens. Katie had solemnly nodded her head, and said, 'Yes, Grandpa,' as if in total acceptance and understanding of what Alan had said.

Neil crept back to the house, feeling it would have been wrong to intrude on such a private moment between grandfather and grand-daughter. He could only surmise that his father did not expect to be alive in October when the baby was due, although he was puzzled by his father speaking to Katie as if there was no doubt whatsoever that she would have a brother.

A wet spring gave way to a surprisingly hot summer. One afternoon, while Neil was with an important client in his office overlooking the park, he was overcome by a sudden light-headed sensation. He left his chair and opened the large window, though the breeze which stirred the trees was warm rather than cool, and not exactly complementary to the air conditioning system either. Neil breathed in the warm city scents, his eyes fixed on Balboa Park. After a moment he sat down again and for the next hour worked diligently with his client. A little after two o'clock, the client left, and Neil's partner, Paul, came in and asked for a particular file. He sat down on the desk while Neil looked for it, remarking that it was too hot to work.

Neil opened a drawer in his filing cabinet then spun sharply round as he heard his father's voice clearly say: 'Well, I guess that's it, Son. Kiss Katie for me, and you take good care now, goodbye.'

Neil stood transfixed with amazement. For a moment he could actually see his father standing before him, a garden trowel in one hand and a bunch of marigolds in the other. He was wearing old trousers and a short-sleeved, plaid shirt.

Neil immediately looked to his partner; surely he would have heard too, the words had been spoken so distinctly. But Paul was still sitting casually on the desk, taking no notice.

Without saying a word to Paul, Neil rushed from the office and within twenty minutes he was at his parents' house.

He opened the door and ran into the living room. He could hear his mother vacuuming one of the bedrooms. Without stopping to let her know he was there, he went out to the garden at the rear.

He found his father lying crumpled on the lawn, a garden trowel in one hand and a bunch of marigolds in the other, wearing his old trousers and a short-sleeved, plaid shirt. He was dead. Even at a glance it was obvious there was nothing anyone could do. In a little while, Neil would go inside and tell his mother, but first he knelt beside his father and with tears streaming down his face, he talked to him for a minute or two, knowing his words would reach his dear dad.

On October the third, Neil's wife gave birth to a baby boy. When Neil took Katie to visit them in the hospital, the little girl was excited. Neil told his wife that he wished his father could see their new baby. Katie laughed, 'But Daddy, Grandpa's here, standing beside Mommy, can't you see him!'

Neil could not, but he believed his daughter. At least he had seen his father on that hot summer's afternoon for a final goodbye, and after all, that was all he had asked for and been promised.

The Evil Governess

Though 'The Evil Governess' was certainly an interesting case to investigate, it was not a pleasant one. It would be no variation on the truth to say there was an element of danger involved, which was why we were called in. One of our female operatives actually received a blow to the back of the neck during the course of the investigation, and before our very eyes, she stumbled across the room from the force of the blow, such was the violence of this disturbance. The percipients' reaction to the haunting was not simply that it was an occasional inconvenience: it actually began to rule their lives. They were appalled by it. Two professional adults, intelligent and well educated, were suddenly made to feel inadequate because they did not know how to deal with this terrible situation that had, out of the blue, disrupted their lives. The worst aspect of this haunting was the fact that the ghost seemed to be intent on causing them harm. This has to be one of the most sinister of the cases on our files.

NICK AND JAY WERE desperate to find someone who could put an end to their weeks of violent torment, or perform whatever was necessary to protect the couple and their two young children from a malevolent entity that stalked the rooms of their house in a small, quiet country village, just inside the county boundary of Greater Manchester.

It had all started eight weeks earlier. They had only moved into the rented house temporarily while they finalised the move into their new house; it was not until they had settled in that there was time to realise everything was not as it should be. Jay felt sure that something unearthly prowled the house, and this opinion seemed to be confirmed by an inexplicable coldness and a terrible smell of decay in the lounge at the front of the house. It was to be the beginning of a long series of events that would inevitably change the couple's lives and ruin any joy they might otherwise have derived from their three months of living in such a large, old residence.

It did not take long after that first indication for the situation to quickly progress.

One day, a painting in the breakfast room, a reproduction of 'The Laughing Cavalier', was found to have been turned upside down, while still hanging from the wall. As Jay went about the house throughout the day, she could feel someone, or something, following and watching her. At times, a peculiar smell accompanied the presence of the unseen intruder.

The handles of several doors were seen to turn and on occasion this was preceded by a knock at the door, but there was never anyone there! Nick even pulled himself out of the bath after he heard someone knock at the bathroom door, and saw the door handle turn as if someone desperately needed to gain entrance to the bathroom: again there was no one there.

One Sunday, while Jay was quietly watching a religious programme on television, she was shocked to hear whistling coming from the hall, harmonising perfectly with a hymn on the telelvision. But Jay was alone in the house at the time!

Again and again someone with a walking stick was heard in the hall, but each time there was nothing to explain the sounds.

The couple were finding it more and more difficult to keep all these strange happenings from the children as the phenomena continued to increase day by day.

Rebecca, the couple's ten-year-old daughter was at first elated to discover a piano in the lounge, and another in the sitting room. She played them both regularly, but her love of music soon diminished when middle C on each piano suddenly and enigmatically ceased to play. Rebecca would not touch the pianos after that day, even though the key on one of them has since been restored, just as mysteriously.

Shortly after, in the early hours of the morning, Jay heard someone talking, the sound coming from the direction of Rebecca's bedroom. She went to investigate but found only Rebecca, who was awake but in bed. When asked to whom she had been talking, Rebecca said she thought it had been her mother standing outside her bedroom door with whom she had conversed, yet Jay had been in her own bedroom when the two-way conversation had attracted her attention.

More than once, the immersion heater was found to be switched on, though the couple never used it, as the back boiler provided all their hot water needs.

The lounge was now becoming quite active, with swirling cold streams snaking their way across the room. Both Nick and Jay felt an ice-cold touch on their faces while in their bedroom above the lounge. The energy was building up, taking on the form of a violent, writhing mass, searching the house, searching and looking for somewhere to *manifest*!

One night, four-year-old Amy awoke from the cries of her sister whom she had dreamt was helplessly caught up in a cyclone. Just moments before, Jay too was awakened by a faint but unequivocal female voice, seemingly coming from downstairs, definitely indicating someone in distress. All that could be found was the menacing cold energy, darting from room to room. Rebecca was fast asleep.

It was decided at this point that Rebecca should move in with Amy. Jay could no longer bear to enter Rebecca's bedroom, and although Amy's bedroom felt distinctly odd, it seemed to be less so than Rebecca's. It was also thought that Amy might be more settled by her sister's company because, ever since the family had moved in, Amy had woken each morning crying and depressed for no obvious reason.

Jay was determined to put these bizarre events out of her mind and began cleaning and rearranging the furniture, which had remained in the house since the previous resident died about ten years before. Jay took a rug out into the rear garden to shake the dust from it, and was returning towards the house when she felt a forceful push on her back, between the shoulder blades. She careered down the gentle slope and found herself sprawling against the wall of the house, under the sitting-room window. She was stunned and confused, and in the most terrible pain. There was no one in the garden to push her, and yet there she lay on the cold, flagged path. Nick was at work, the children at school, and Jay was too weak to shout for a neighbour's help. All she could do was crawl, as best she could, into the house to telephone for help.

At the hospital, the doctors remarked that Jay's broken arm and foot were far too severe for a simple fall and concluded that she must have been pushed with a violent force.

There then followed a remission in the phenomena of about a month, a period of grace for which the couple were thankful, while they tried to understand all that had been happening during the previous three weeks. Only the continued cold spots and odours plagued them as they searched for some explanation.

No answers were forthcoming, but something else was! The evil torment struck unexpectedly on November 3rd, 1987. Jay was sitting in an armchair with her injured foot resting on a piano stool; Amy was with her and seated on the arm of the couch. Suddenly and without warning, Amy was lifted up and thrown from the couch, landing some 120 centimetres away, against the door of the sitting room. She was unhurt, but the activity was building up again, little by little, becoming more and more threatening.

On Saturday afternoon, four days later, Jay was again relaxing her injured foot on the piano stool when, suddenly, the stool was whisked away from her by an invisible hand and her foot was sent painfully crashing to the floor. Later that day, she lit a cigarette, which burst into flames along its entire length. The hall was full of noises coming from the ghostly, clumping, walking stick. A wedge of dreadful cold cut its way into the sitting room. The lounge door opened by itself, and ornaments on the piano in the lounge were found to have moved without anyone having been in the room.

That evening, the cold entered the sitting room in great swathes, creating a numbing chill in the room, despite the roaring coal fire. Jay and Nick feared for the safety of themselves and their two young girls. Jay had already expressed a particular fear of the stairs, as she felt that someone wanted to push her down them — and when it did happen to Amy that Saturday, it added greatly to the confirmation of Jay's fears. Amy was coming downstairs, and as she started her descent of the bottom flight, she was lifted up, again by invisible hands, and thrown down the remaining steps.

The disturbance was quickly gaining strength; it was only four days between the two attacks on Amy, the second being more threatening than the first. It was certain that there would be another attack within the next week, and one of even more severity. Amy had been lucky to escape injury so far, but the suppleness of a four-year-old's body did not make Amy indestructible.

But would Amy be the next victim? Would the evil presence injure her as it had Jay — in a systematic frenzy? Or would it choose a new, and unsuspecting prey?

These questions and more needed answering. Yet these questions in particular made it impossible to allow the entity an opportunity to provide the answers. The next occurrence of the malevolent phenomena had somehow to be stopped and now!

During the investigative team's first visit to the house on a dismal Sunday afternoon in November, Dianne, one of the team's investigators, saw a young boy at an upstairs window, as she approached the front door from outside the house. No details of the family had been mentioned to the team, so Dianne was not even aware at the time, that she could only have seen a ghost. Only the team leader knew there was no son in the family, and that the couple had arranged for the two girls to be out of the house for the visit.

There had been no previous mention of a sighting, though Jay now admitted she had seen the ghostly figure of a woman pass the sitting room window. Nick mentioned some photographs of the owner's family that had been left in a drawer. When they were shown to Dianne, she identified positively the younger of two brothers as the boy she had seen at the window of what she later discovered was Amy's bedroom.

From this lead, it was possible to verify quickly the identity of the youth, and to learn the enlightening historical details surrounding him.

The main ghost, however, was a strict disciplinarian in life, although cruel bully is a more fitting description. She lived as a governess in the house with two other ladies and the two young boys. This vicious governess was undoubtedly the stronger personality and not a person to be contested. What was very evident was that she frequently beat the two young boys with a monstrous fury, using the same walking stick which supported an injury to her left leg. She could be heard anywhere in the house by the clump, clump of her stick; often she would bang it against the wall as she walked towards the boys' bedrooms to give them another beating. The older boy had become hardened to it to some extent and would rebel against her, but this made her even more determined to hurt him, which in consequence brought more hurt to the youngest who was very emotional and cried almost constantly, either from his own beatings or in sympathy for his elder brother.

Most of the beatings occurred in the elder brother's bedroom, the room Jay had moved Rebecca from because she could not stand its atmosphere. Rebecca was moved in with Amy, the bedroom once occupied by the younger brother and where he spent so many endless hours, crying to himself. Amy had been unknowingly soaking up these sad emotions, while she was asleep, hence she would awake depressed and crying.

Some remarkable similarities proved important issues in this case. During the lifetime of the ghostly governess, there were two other adults and two children living in the house, just as at that present time. It is also significant that the children were of the same sex in both situations even though the two girls were of opposite sex to the two boys in the past. This formula alone has been known to activate a haunting under the right conditions, especially when the occurrence seeks the repetition of past events and even tries to regenerate its power by moulding the present to fit the past situation exactly.

During the course of this transformation, therefore, Jay's character became very similar to that of the governess: she developed a menacing fury inside, that could erupt at any moment without reason, or warning. This was not Jay's normal character. Even her physical appearance was alarmingly indicative of the evil presence trying to mould Jay in its own image; the injury to the left leg, the change in character, facial expression; then presumably, the final transition of beating the children without mercy. It was a veritable house of horrors.

When Jay mentioned that she was using a walking stick from the hall since her misfortune in the garden, it brought to mind the chilling possibility that she might even be using the same walking stick which once belonged to the governess. It served to remind the team that both Jay and the wicked ghost needed to support an injured left leg.

Although the haunting would have been suitable for further study and training of investigators, the governess was promptly exorcised for the family's protection during their last few weeks in the house.

Amy's room was also vacated, as the emotional horror which took place there, has seeped into the very brickwork and will take centuries to dissolve. The room, now sealed, awaits future research. Or the next unsuspecting family to unleash the memory of its mournful past.

Runaway

This case was a difficult one to handle. As in the best detective stories, there appeared several red herrings, and twists and turns to the plot. Our original approach had to be changed, and at one point legal advice sought, as we were most anxious to comply with the laws of the state, and not — albeit inadvertently — be seen to condone certain practices which were going on at the site of the haunting. The neighbours' involvement was of tremendous value, and would be a credit to any neighbourhood watch scheme. Their organisation, and reports were exemplary, and aided us greatly in the investigation.

STRANGE VOICES, NOISES and flickering lights in an old, vacant house in Los Angeles, California, during the first five months of 1987, led local residents to believe it was haunted. Their attempts to dispel the fearsome rumours only served to strengthen the reality of such fears, but there were some uncanny surprises waiting to be discovered.

Mr B. was the first resident to brave a closer look at the house. He was sceptical about the possibility of spooks taking over the building and approached without fear. It was his theory that vagrants had somehow gained access to the house and he was more than ready to throw them out. However, the doors and windows were all securely locked and Mr B. could see no means of entrance without a key. He peered through each window within reach, but could not make out any detail because even in broad daylight the house was dark inside. He left with the impression that no one was living there, least of all vagrants.

The sinister incidents continued, even though Mr B. was not the only one to look for a natural explanation and come away disappointed.

Perhaps once or twice a week, someone casually walking past the house would report hearing muffled voices coming from inside, but on stopping to listen more intently, the voices gradually faded away until they blended into, and became lost in, the natural background noise of the surrounding environment. It was a frustrating predicament for those who, at one moment, were absolutely certain that they heard the voices, and yet in the next, the voices were gone, without actually seeming to stop. Nevertheless, the voices were heard in the same puzzling way by several witnesses — during the day, evening, and into the early hours of the night. The only difference was the extent to which witnesses thought their imaginations were playing tricks on them.

Occasionally, an isolated noise could be heard distinctly: a can dropping to the floor, the banging of a door, metallic sounds, shuffling noises, and even more alarmingly real, the sound of the toilet being flushed, and infrequent wisps of smoke seen coming from the chimney.

A stranger to the area could not be blamed for assuming that the house was occupied by an elderly recluse who, for whatever reason, had no wish to use the convenience of electric lighting. The neighbours knew that the owner was not living there at the present time, because they surely would have seen him if he had returned home.

Dave had lived in the house for some years with his wife, who gave birth to a baby girl in 1985. Almost a year later, she left him, taking the baby with her. Dave was devastated, and it was obvious that he would have gone after her and begged her to return if only he knew where she had gone. Three months later, however, when he sold his car and departed with his overnight bag as he had done so many times in the past, the neighbours were relieved, for it suggested he had started to recover from his trauma and was going abroad again with his work.

It was about a year later when the activity started, and at first it was thought Dave had finished his contract abroad and returned home. His absence from the local scene was soon noticed, however, creating much doubt. Finally, after a few days, a complete reversal of the initial surmise was prompted by no confirmation of his presence. There was no reason to assume Dave had returned and locked himself away in the house; he was the sociable type who would have made the short walk to the local bar within a day of arriving home. Within a week, he would have bought another car and the whole street would have heard where he had been working. At the very least, someone would have been sure to see him during the previous five months, but no one had. The mysterious lights and noises, however, were witnessed with increasing frequency, but in a securely locked house, these did not conform with any natural explanation.

Almost every night, the strange flickering lights were observed in the house, sometimes a discernible shadow would be seen as it moved across a window. The outline was blurred but opinion was soon held that the ghost was a woman rather than a man.

This seemed to be confirmed by Mr B's brief sighting of a young girl

131

in the garden behind the house. He was once more checking on the security of the building, and had started moving along the narrow walkway between the shrub hedge and the side of the house, towards the rear. Suddenly he was surprised by the figure of a teenage girl wearing dark clothes who, on seeing him, dashed towards the back door. Mr B. shouted to her but she paid him no heed. He started to give chase but was obstructed in his quest by a freak wind which blew several branches of the hedge across his face. It delayed him only for a few seconds before fighting his way through and arriving at the door. He found it securely locked and there was no sign of the young girl.

He was certain she was inside the house, as there was nowhere else she could have hidden that quickly. Mr B. tried unsuccessfully to force the door open, and began hammering on it with his fist and shouting for the girl to come out, or he would have to call the police. Except for a single sound of something heavy dropping to the floor inside, all was quiet. He knew she held the upper hand, for while he went home to phone the police department, she could easily steal away and he would have no evidence to support his fleeting glimpse of an intruder. Due to his annoyance at the situation, he threw his weight at the door with more determination. Then a roofing tile fell to the ground, narrowly missing his shoulder. Mr B. stepped back with the shock of its closeness, and just in time avoided the next tile which fell to the exact spot where he had been standing a second earlier.

He backed further away from the house so he could see the roof clearly. There were no loose roofing tiles to be seen and none missing, but he decided his course of action was futile and returned home.

When Mr B. told his wife of the young girl, Mrs B. immediately queried his description: the only descriptions so far reported were of the ghostly figure at the window, which characterised a female with long, blonde hair, whereas, Mr B. claimed his encounter was with a young girl with short, black hair. This caused Mr B. himself to question what he had seen, and to resist his earlier intention of contacting the police department. After all, he would look a fool giving a description which contradicted that of several neighbours who had seen the figure more than once, and for longer than a brief moment, especially after the police might have forced their way into the house only to find it empty. But for his scepticism, he might readily have believed he had seen a ghost rather than an elusive teenager. He doubted that Dave would leave his house unlocked while he was away, and there was nothing to indicate access had been gained by force, so Mr B. did not know what to believe any more.

The eerie lights and shadows were not seen for four days after Mr

B's sighting. The voices, however, continued, as did the noises.

Another strange sighting took place about a week later, when another neighbour, while passing Dave's house, caught a brief glimpse of not one, but two young girls in the back garden. He ran down the side of the house, but again the garden was empty and the house secure. His description added more to Mr B's confusion, for it was of two blonde girls.

By now, there was little argument to support anything but a supernatural explanation. Normal access to the house proved impossible and the voices and noises were becoming louder and more frequent.

A brief sighting several weeks later, by another neighbour, Mr S., of a man and a young girl in the garden behind Dave's house, seemed to suggest that the house was attracting more and more ghosts. There was less time on this occasion to record much detail, except that the man was tall, and the girl had dark hair and wore what seemed to be a yellow sweater, without which the figures may not have been noticed at all.

The sporadic sightings were enough to conclude that the haunting of Dave's vacant house was somehow dependent on the regular comings and goings, but it was only when an organised surveillance was set up and working round the clock, that the sinister facts of this case came to light.

The observation point, on the landing of a nearby house, provided a good view of all entrances to the grounds of Dave's house even though it was not possible to see the doors.

A schedule was drawn up within the week to illustrate the sightings in the garden, which were only observed between the hours of one o'clock in the afternoon and two o'clock in the morning. It was a long way from being a conclusive document, because only four instances were recorded.

On three separate afternoons, two or three young girls were seen departing from Dave's house, the same returning, three or four hours later. Some of the girls carried a bag, which appeared to be fuller on their return than it was when they left. An estimate by computer analysis determined each bag to weigh between 0.9 and 2.7 kilogrammes, heavier on the returning journey.

Once, during the early hours of the morning, two girls emerged from the garden shortly before midnight, coming back about two hours later, with a third girl.

To add credence to the girls' elusive quality, investigators trying to follow the girls on their journeys, were unable to track them through the crowded Los Angeles city streets during the day. The attempt to follow them at night, however, was foiled by the exact opposite: deserted back streets, which made it impossible to trail them unseen.

After each time girls left or returned to the house, the building was manually surveyed almost immediately. The only normal assumption to be made was that a key was being used to gain entrance.

All the sightings confirmed earlier reports of the girls being visibly solid, but their behaviour did not correspond to that of any paranormal entity. This was painfully evident when, two days later, three investigators managed to capture one of the girls in the next street as she was returning to the house: no ghost has *ever* kicked, scratched and bitten an investigator.

This girl was certainly not a supernatural being. Even though she possessed superhuman strength and behaved like a wild animal, she was without a doubt, a normal earthly teenager, albeit terrified and initially extremely hostile. The bedraggled young woman eventually succumbed to the 'charm' of three burly investigators, and slowly the astonishing truth began to unfold.

Debbie, at nineteen years old, was the eldest of seven teenagers living in the house, the youngest being twelve. All were runaways, for one reason or another.

This signalled an end to the investigation, with only a few curious details requiring an explanation.

When asked about the man who was first sighted briefly by Mr S., and in all was only seen twice, the girls revealed it was Dave, the owner of the house, but they did not know where he was at that time. Apparently, he only came to the house once in a while to see that everything was alright. It would seem Dave had returned after all.

The bizarre story started when Sarah, at fourteen years old, arrived in Los Angeles. She had no money and was pitifully trying to hustle small change when she encountered Dave. He took her to his house saying she could stay there under the condition that she shared the goodwill with other youngsters who were in similar need of shelter. Sarah had been living in the house for the past six months, over which time, she recruited the other runaways.

Frequently, Dave returned to tell Sarah of another youngster who would be arriving in Los Angeles later that day, whom she was to meet and bring back to the house. On each occasion, Dave stated the time of arrival, the location of the pick-up and an adequate description, all of which proved correct.

The teenagers were questioned at length to determine if this man was really Dave. Some information about him could obviously be gathered simply from living in his home, but other answers could not be dismissed so easily, such as an accurate description of Dave's last car, as well as the name and location of Dave's friend who bought the car, an event which occurred some eighteen months before, and one year before Sarah arrived. Even Dave's neighbours did not know who bought the car.

There was an increasing need to interview the elusive Dave, and work was already in hand towards tracing him.

Meanwhile, Sarah was anxious about meeting someone at the bus station at seven o'clock that evening. Caution was demanded, and it was eventually agreed that Debbie and two investigators would attend the rendezvous. Their instructions were to meet a young woman with short auburn hair, wearing a beige raincoat and carrying a baby and a large brown bag.

True enough, a little after seven o'clock, a woman emerged from the bus station fitting this description. Debbie immediately ran towards her, they talked, and a few minutes later, approached the two onlooking investigators in anticipation of the return journey.

The newcomer was silent on the short drive back, but when she entered Dave's house, the young woman exclaimed in surprise and confusion at the many unfamiliar faces. Nevertheless she succeeded in shocking everyone there, by immediately asking where Dave was.

The young woman explained that she was Mari, Dave's wife. She had returned to Los Angeles with no particular plans of running back to Dave, though she did hope they would meet and start a new relationship. For now, Mari was content to stay in the familiar house and somewhat relieved she did not have to face Dave while in her present state of turmoil.

There was no doubt whatsoever that Dave was responsible for moulding this complex situation. But when he was eventually traced through his employer abroad, it was discovered that Dave had died in an automobile accident about two months *before* Sarah met him and was taken back to his house.

The ghost of Dave has not been reported since. Mari still lives in the house, having started a small business producing macramé. Debbie also lives there as well as one of the fifteen-year-olds, who, with the consent of her parents is learning the art of macramé, and is in a location where at least they know she is safe and can be visited. She also attends school in Los Angeles, which she rarely did in her home town.

The remaining five teenagers returned home to their respective families; two have since run away again. It can only be hoped that they find similarly safe shelter from the world of vice at their destinations, whether ghostly or otherwise.

A Real Little Girl

Even the unsentimental and unimaginative will appreci-
ate the pathos of this case. The couple involved reported
the phenomena the following week because they felt it
would give courage to others who had suffered a similar
tragedy. Their honesty was as transparent as glass, but
solid indisputable proof is no easy taskmaster, and it
took a supreme effort of will on their part to undergo the
investigation and share every intimate detail of their
heart-rending experience. The stranger at the church,
who held such a vital role, was later traced, and was more
shy of giving her statement than the couple were. So, all
in all, it was a difficult case to investigate, though we
consider ourselves lucky, as there are many reports of
this type of haunting which simple cannot be proven.

S UPERFICIALLY, ALEX AND Karen Moss seemed to live an
idyllic life. They were childhood sweethearts and had married
when both of them were in their early twenties. Alex, a builder by
trade, had used his skill expertly in renovating their beautiful,
seventeenth-century, stone-built house in the heart of what was once
a large sheep-walk in twelfth-century England. The area later
became known as the Cotswolds. The couple were financially secure, had the support and affection of devoted parents, and were
both extremely happy with their chosen way of life.

After two years of marriage, their daughter, Carol Ann, was born.
To Alex and Karen, their happiness seemed to be complete. But two
weeks after Carol Ann's fifth birthday, disaster struck. Carol Ann
died, a victim of meningitis.

The young couple were inconsolable and cut themselves off from
family and friends. Their grief was such that their whole way of life
was changed overnight. They had no interest in visiting anyone, and
when family or friends visited them, the couple found it difficult even
to converse. They would sit side by side, both seeming to be lost in
private contemplation. Alex no longer played golf on Sundays, and
Karen no longer went riding on Saturdays.

Before Carol Ann's death, Karen had been a regular churchgoer; now she could not even bear to set foot inside the pretty village church.

Often, though, she would spend hours in the little churchyard at the back of the church, sitting on a wooden bench, just a few steps from Carol Ann's grave. She still felt deep maternal instincts for her child, and ached to be able to hold her little girl, to hear her laugh, to care for her needs again. If only she knew that Carol Ann was safe, cared for, was not afraid and pining for the mother and father who had been so devoted to her.

Karen had always believed in an afterlife, but now she was no longer sure. She tried desperately to imagine her daughter in some kind of heavenly existence, loved and cared for as she had been in life, but such imaginings would not form properly. Karen was sure she was heading for a nervous breakdown.

Come rain or shine she would trek to the churchyard, sit on the wooden bench, and torture herself with memories of her daughter. If only she could receive some kind of sign which would offer her reassurance of her daughter's well-being, she felt that at least there would be a chance of living a semblance of that former way of life. Of course, she would always miss Carol Ann, and long with all her heart and soul to have her little girl back, but at least the destructive element would be taken out of the pain that she felt.

Seven, long, heart-breaking months after Carol Ann's death, a strange incident occurred in the Moss family home. Alex had always been careless with his car keys, often absent-mindedly tossing the keys down somewhere in the lounge or kitchen, then having to hunt for them when they were needed later. One afternoon, as he was rummaging frantically in the lounge, he asked Karen if she had seen his keys as he could not find them. The couple searched high and low. Then a thought struck Karen, and she went over to a wooden shelf set in the stone chimney breast; she looked in the flowered jar which sat there, and extracted Alex's car keys.

They were both astounded. The little jar had been bought for Karen by Carol Ann, while having a day out with her grandmother, and the little girl had been in the habit of popping her daddy's car keys in it for safe keeping whenever she spotted them lying around. Karen had no idea what had prompted her to look inside this little jar, as neither of them ever, even inadvertently, put anything into the ornament.

Karen wondered if this was at last the sign she had wished and prayed for, an indication that her daughter lived on in some way. This thought cheered her to an extent for the next few days. Then, as doubt crept in, Karen slipped back into the former, dismal stupor which had claimed her since Carol Ann's death.

One morning, a few weeks later, Karen was cleaning the master bedroom when she noticed something amiss. Going over to the dressing table, she saw that her daughter's make-up bag was there. It was open, but nothing removed.

Karen sat on the bed, her mind racing. Carol Ann had always been fascinated by her mother's make-up and her jars of cream and perfume, to the extent that Karen had bought her some toy replicas of her make-up items, and also saved pots and make-up containers when empty, washing these out and adding them to Carol Ann's collection, which was kept in the plump, floral, make-up bag Karen had given to her daughter. It was this bulging bag which now sat on Karen's dressing table. It was not there when Karen had got up that morning; in fact, the last time she had seen it was when she put it with the rest of Carol Ann's toys and books in Carol Ann's room after she died.

Karen could not even bring herself to touch this bag now. She would ask Alex to put it back in Carol Ann's room later. So she sat there on the bed and wept, wondering how she was ever going to cope with the loss of her daughter.

Just weeks later when Easter Sunday arrived, Karen was tempted to go to church as she used to, but she could not face it. All her ingrained religious beliefs had ceased to exist along with her daughter.

That afternoon, with Alex to accompany her, they went to the churchyard taking some flowers for Carol Ann's grave. It was a warm sunny day for the time of year. As they placed the flowers and stood hand in hand by the graveside, Karen felt she could no longer go on. She was indifferent to the beauty around her, the blue sky, the twitter of birds, the gentle breeze which combed the grass and was heavy with the scent of flowers; Karen felt she may as well be buried here with her daughter for all that life meant to her any more.

In silence the couple walked along the narrow winding path, paying no attention to their surroundings. Thus, they did not notice the approaching middle-aged lady a short distance ahead of them, who, after placing flowers on a grave, had stepped onto the same path, which wound its way to the side and then the front of the church.

The lady stopped and smiled at them, her face so radiant with pleasure, that Alex and Karen wondered if they knew her. But she was a stranger to them.

As they came up beside her, she spoke to them with a kind, cheerful voice. 'What a beautiful little girl you have,' the lady announced, still smiling.

Karen felt her blood turn cold, she gripped Alex's arm, and was bereft of speech. She could only stare at the woman as if she were mad. Something of this was obviously felt by the stranger, as the lady leaned to one side to peer around them. 'I cannot see her now,' she remarked, her brow creasing in puzzlement.

Karen and Alex looked around but could see nothing. Karen gripped the woman's arm. 'What did she look like?' she begged.

The lady hesitated for a moment, hardly knowing what to make of Karen's bizarre and somewhat unexpected reaction to her complimentary observation. Then she gave a description: a tall young girl, very pretty, blonde hair tied back with a pink ribbon. A pink jacket and white dress, with thin, delicate, pink stripes, white knee socks and shoes, and carrying a 'My Little Pony' bag. She had been skipping along a few steps behind them both, and then seemed to dart behind a headstone; the lady assumed the child was playing a game, waiting for her parents to notice her absence and come looking for her.

Karen swayed, colour drained from her face and a moan escaped from her lips. The woman helped to steer her quickly to a nearby wooden bench, asking whatever was wrong. Alex explained about their daughter's death, and that the description of the little girl, in every detail, fitted their daughter.

The stranger now turned as pale as the couple were, but after a few moments, regaining her composure, she exclaimed that the girl had looked so real, and told of how she had just straightened up after placing flowers on her own mother's grave when she had spotted the child, and thought the couple fortunate to have such a beautiful daughter, especially as the little girl seemed to have such a happy, contented disposition, smiling to herself as she skipped along behind her parents.

It was because the little girl did not reappear from behind the headstone and the couple looked so shocked by her revealing testimony, that the woman had cause to wonder just what she had stumbled into. Never before in her life had she seen a ghost, and she was deeply sorry that having done so now, had caused the young couple such utter distress.

At this point, Karen wept openly. When she could finally speak, she assured the stranger that she had done them a tremendous service. She had given them back the will to go on with life.

Later, when Karen and Alex were back at home, Karen realised that she had not even asked the woman her name. She went up to her daughter's bedroom, and said a prayer. She had been given the sign she longed for, and knew now that her darling Carol Ann lived on. Opening the wardrobe, Karen took out the white dress with the thin, delicate, pink stripes. It had always been Carol Ann's favourite dress. Closing her eyes, she sent out her thoughts to her daughter, knowing now, that she had not completely lost the child she would love for the rest of her life, and beyond.

Secret Visitations

A member of the medical profession reported this case to us. She was no stranger to experiencing ghosts, though it is interesting to note that on this occasion, she was both shocked and horrified by her failure to recognise this particular manifestation as a ghost. This does not cast doubt on her statement, instead, it actually adds to its authenticity, as the case presents a different type of occurrence than she had been accustomed to witness. Here we have a ghost with a purpose, and once the purpose was achieved, was not seen again. It was a sighting of a ghost oblivious to its surroundings and the presence of others within close proximity, a sighting, spontaneous and natural, of a ghost seemingly more natural than the events which followed. Many unique lessons can be learned about the supernatural, so when the reporter learned some of them the hard way, she was determined to protect others from a similar destiny — which is why she reported it the following morning, still in the wake of unfortunate devastation.

ELIZABETH SUFFERED FROM terminal cancer. As she lay in bed at the specialised women's hospital, her pain alleviated by drugs which also distorted her mind, there was no doubt that she would die; the only unanswered question being when.

She had been born on Christmas Day, almost eighty years earlier, and for as long as anyone could remember, Elizabeth always said she would die on her birthday. As her eightieth birthday approached, no one thought now of such a remarkable coincidence: it was all in God's hands at this late stage.

Three weeks before Christmas and just over a week after Elizabeth's admittance to hospital, her husband, Harry, also became ill and was admitted to a nearby hospital. The next time Elizabeth's daughter, Trudy, and her family visited Elizabeth, they decided to say nothing to her about Harry's illness. Elizabeth knew Harry was too infirm to visit her, and as there was every chance of him recovering, there was no point in upsetting Elizabeth.

It was a decision made harder by the fact that Elizabeth never failed to ask about both Harry, and her cat. After a few days, the deceit proved too upsetting for Trudy's young children and they were subsequently excluded from further visits. The ward sister was made fully aware of the situation, as Trudy and the sister had become quite friendly. However, the sister promised to adhere to the secrecy as a precaution against Elizabeth asking questions of the other staff.

Hard though it was to visit both her parents in different hospitals, Trudy managed remarkably well. Both she and her husband worked shifts, and between them they made sure of someone visiting each aging parent twice every day. Friends, neighbours and relatives were allowed to visit only after Trudy's warning not to mention the health of one parent to the other, for the conspiracy contained a double secret as Harry did not know that Elizabeth would spend the last days of her life in hospital, and he too continued to ask how his wife was and when she could go home.

Harry's condition was much more severe than anyone suspected, however, and just a week before Christmas, he died in hospital. This fact too was shielded from Elizabeth. It was certain the shock of finding out would kill her and the family could only continue the charade in the hope of Elizabeth spending her final days in peaceful contentment. Harry's death became the family's most closely guarded secret from Elizabeth. No one at the women's hospital was informed and no announcement was made in the local obituary column.

The following day, when Trudy's husband returned from his visit to Elizabeth, he wore a puzzled expression, which he explained to Trudy as being the result of a comment made by her mother. Instead of asking about Harry and the cat as she always did previously, this time she had asked about her grandchildren and the cat. From then on, Elizabeth always asked about the grandchildren and the cat, with no reference whatsoever to Harry.

Trudy and her husband both shared the uncalming thought that Elizabeth somehow knew that Harry had died, but it was plainly impossible, and so the reason for this change was attributed to the effect on her mind of the strong drugs needed to kill the pain of the cancer. After all, there were many days when Elizabeth failed even to recognise her own daughter because of the drugs. Indeed it was a miracle she could remember that she *had* a cat, let alone ask how it was doing, and be anxious about it missing her companionship.

· On Christmas Day, Trudy and her family went to the women's hospital to visit Elizabeth, taking along Christmas and birthday presents for her and a bouquet of flowers. The patient seemed much brighter than she had been lately, though was too exhausted and trance-like from the drugs to fully enjoy the spirit of the day. The visitors told her not to worry about Harry as they would be paying him a visit that afternoon and taking along a present for him. It was not really a lie, for they were indeed going straight from the hospital to the cemetery where Harry had been buried. Harry's present currently lay in their station wagon outside the hospital; it was a second bouquet of flowers for his graveside. Of course, they intended that Elizabeth would assume that Harry was just as infirm as he had been for a long time and that they would be visiting him at home. Nevertheless, they were mindful of Elizabeth's reaction, but she just smiled weakly at her daughter, then fell asleep still holding her birthday and Christmas presents.

When finally the family arrived home, it was time to prepare the evening meal, but this was abandoned due to a phone call from the hospital informing Trudy that her mother had died peacefully in her sleep that afternoon. True to her word, Elizabeth *had* died on her birthday.

Trudy and her husband returned to the hospital in the evening to make the necessary arrangements. As a result of their friendship through the frequent visits, the ward sister wasted no time in comforting Trudy when she broke down in tears in her office. Soon, through a haze of emotion, Trudy expressed regret that both her parents had died without ever being able to comfort each other during their final days, adding that they were completely devoted to each other. Her words were barely intelligible through weeping.

The sister was kindly sympathetic towards them and tried to reassure them in offering a simple statement that Harry *had* comforted Elizabeth, during his visit earlier that afternoon.

Trudy and her husband were repulsed by the sister's comment. They both thought it in extremely bad taste for her to lie cruelly to them about Harry having visited Elizabeth.

The ward sister now learned for the first time of Harry's death. Instinctively, she dismissed it as impossible. After all, she had seen him herself. He had come every day for the past week to see Elizabeth. There was no mistake, as Elizabeth had often shown the staff Harry's photograph which she proudly displayed by her bedside, and the sister was not the only one to see him, for several of the nurses also had seen Harry when he came.

In fact, Harry had been with Elizabeth just before she died. When the doctor came to look in on her, he thought it best to defer his examination until Harry had gone because he too recognised him as Elizabeth's husband. He marvelled at the two of them laughing together and enjoying each other's company, even remarking to the nurse that he wished all his patients were so lively. It was indeed a cheerful sight, and a welcomed one in a ward where most patients find their last few days of life such an exhausting battle. Later, when the doctor returned, Harry had gone and Elizabeth was at peace.

Realising later that Trudy could hardly be mistaken about her own father's death, the ward sister apologised for her thoughtlessness, explaining that she would often see ghosts in her job, either solid or wispy, transient figures, but when she had seen Harry sitting beside Elizabeth's bed, she had naturally assumed he had recovered from his illness and was now well enought to visit his wife. Not for one minute had she thought that she was actually seeing Harry's ghost.

Not Mortal

This case came to our attention through a survey we were
conducting in the area. One can perhaps imagine our
surprise and delight when Mark Foster came to his door,
and, after the usual preliminaries, stated in the most
down-to-earth manner that he had experienced this
apparition. But for the survey, we would never have
known about it, as Mark is of a reticent nature, and the
sort of person to shy away from attention. Chance intervened here in that our survey had been postponed for
a month due to the workload at the time, otherwise it
would have taken place two days before the sighting —
and it is unlikely that Mark would have made an un-
prompted report.

MARK FOSTER WHISTLED cheerfully as he rode his
bicycle home. He had enjoyed his customary two pints of
beer in the Black Horse, so was naturally feeling quite mellow. The
bicycle was actually his mother's; waste not want not, was an
aphorism adhered to by the Fosters, despite the fact that they were
comfortably well-off. Mark looked decidedly incongruous as he
peddled along, his towering frame of sheer muscle and bulk giving
the impression that he was a giant, riding on a toy vehicle.

It was nearly eleven o'clock at night when Mark, still whistling,
as was his habit — beer or no beer — approached the vicinity of the
churchyard. This quiet country lane was deserted, giving Mark the
impression that he had the sparsely populated little village all to
himself. The silver moonlight illuminated well, picking out the detail
of the sixteenth-century church in stark relief against a soft, dove-
grey, summer sky. Not even a hint of a breeze was evident, all and
everything was as still as a painting. Only the isolated screech of an
owl and muted scurrying sounds of rural, night animals disturbed
the silence, along with Mark's whistling and the mechanical squeaks
and creaks of his bike; it had protested thus for years, so Mark
therefore paid its grumblings no heed.

However, he had just come level with the lychgate of St
Michael's, when the front wheel wobbled alarmingly. Mark sighed,

dismounted and bent down to take a look, leaning the bike against the stone wall which surrounded the churchyard.

The wheel had worked loose and needed attention, but as Mark had no tools with him, it meant carrying the machine home. He was only five minutes away from the cottage where he lived with his widowed mother, so Mark was not overly concerned. He had spent a pleasant evening in the Black Horse enjoying the lively company of his two pals, and it was a fine, warm night. Besides, it would take considerably more than a faulty wheel and a short walk home to dispel Mark's reliable sunny nature, which had given him the nickname in the village of the Gentle Giant.

So, with a shrug of his shoulders and the habitual whistle, Mark prepared to set off. The tune died on his lips, however. The bike slid from his grasp, and a puzzled frown creased his wide brow. He shook his head, as if to clear his senses, then looked again.

His eyesight was excellent, besides, it was a crystal clear night, and the moonlight lit up the surrounding countryside in a wash of soft shades that would have inspired any artist or poet.

Summoning every ounce of concentration Mark scrutinised the area of churchyard directly in front of him, the bike discarded at his feet and his two, huge, work-worn hands leaning heavily on the rough stone wall. He nodded his head with satisfaction: he had not been seeing things. His attention was riveted to the spot now, and he lost all concept of time, while he watched with absolute, heart-pounding fascination as a sylphlike figure appeared to drift across the dry grass. The lady, for he thought of her as such, was slender in the extreme. Elegant, lovely, delicate as a flower, thought Mark, who was struck with a dumb admiration. She was no more than six metres away. And though Mark had first thought that it might be some lass from the village who, for reasons best known to herself, had chosen to flit about the headstones, both old and ancient, in the parody of a midsummer dance, that original fleeting thought had now been dismissed. She looked real enough, too darn real for comfort, but there was about her an otherworldliness which was categorically undeniable.

If anyone had ever asked Mark Foster if he believed in ghosts, he would probably have considered the question earnestly for a moment, and then pronounced that as he had never seen one, he could not rightly say. But from this night on, Mark would swear with all honesty that he saw this 'Lady', and she was not of the stuff mere mortals are made of.

And so, Mark stood there, the only living soul in that country lane, with fields stretching to the horizon on one side of the lane, and St Michael's standing before him, eerie, ethereal, and glorious in its mantle of moonlight, while the 'Lady' danced on.

She weaved about, lingered for a fleeting moment here and there, then off she went again, around the headstones, following the narrow path one moment then off across the grass another. Her hair was the colour of pewter in the moonlight, long and slightly wavy. Her garment seemed as transparent as mist, giving the impression that she was naked beneath, yet hers was a sexless form, no curve of thighs or swell of breast, more a willowy figure, bending this way and that, as if every movement was brought about by an erratic unknown breeze.

At last, she came to a headstone which claimed her attention; she swirled around it, more than once, then, in the blink of an eye, she was gone. Mark heard his own breath expelled from his lungs. So fascinated had he been, that he had been barely breathing the entire time, his whole body stiff now from standing so perfectly still and rigid. And still his eyes were fastened on the grave, for about sixty centimetres above it lay, in perfect formation, a sheet of mist.

He must have stood there for five minutes or more, while the mist remained suspended. He shuddered now, and could take no more. Mark Foster was not superstitious, but this he felt was for God's eyes only and not for such as himself. There was something sacred about it, beyond this world, and he longed with a desperation to be home in the cosy, familiar kitchen, and distanced from it all.

Even so, he did not hurry. Slow ponderous steps took him home. He was shaken, haunted by what he had seen and bereft of speech when his mother greeted his arrival. He hardly heard a word she said, automatically shaking his head as she offered to make his supper. Mrs Foster was puzzled, naturally. As a rule, Mark was an unobtrusive lad, but not averse to a bit of a chitchat, and always ready for a bite of supper and a mug of tea before going to bed, but tonight he could not get upstairs fast enough.

At breakfast, Mark was again uncommunicative, answering his mother's questions as briefly as possibly: yes, he did have a nice evening; yes, his pals Ed and Mike had been in the pub; yes, he was alright, why shouldn't he be? When he finally complained: 'Don't fuss, Mum,' Mrs Foster gave up her questioning, silently joined her son at the table, and tucked in to her eggs and bacon.

There was plenty of work to be done that morning on their land, as they had a market garden. At lunch time, Mrs Foster realised that any conversation would have to come from her, and began to chat about general things, then mentioned the funeral.

Her son's head came up with a jolt. 'What funeral was this then?' he demanded to know.

'Why, Megan Lipton's of course,' she explained. Then she laughed, 'Oh she were a one was Megan.' Mrs Foster had gone to school with her, and they had lived in the same village all their lives. 'Surely you remember me talking about her on occasions?' she asked her son.

146

Mark nodded his head, still lost in thought. Yes, he recalled Megan Lipton. Not that he had seen much of her over the years, as she had lived on the other side of the village and was something of a recluse. His mind conjured up the vague image of a willowy woman in her middle forties, who had always given him a smile whenever he saw her in her garden.

'After their parents died,' Mrs Foster reflected, between mouthfuls of food, 'Megan and her brother, Angus, had shared the cottage. A right spritely one was Megan, full of life and mischief, but Angus, oh, rotten to the core was that one. Discouraged every young chap who had an eye for her, and made her life hell he did.

'It was not easy in them days for a lass to just take herself off. Besides, Megan had a good heart and would not have deserted her brother. He had terrible health though, and died before he were thirty-five. Megan could hardly hide her joy of being free of him at his funeral, and there had been many to notice it too. There was a good turn-out considering what a nasty belligerent swine he was.

'Megan lived with a chap she had taken a fancy to after that, and not one person condemned her for it either.'

Mark interrupted this speech: 'And it's Megan's funeral today, is it?'

Mrs Foster shook her head. 'No! 'That were yesterday.' She laughed again, 'I don't reckon she's much taken with being buried in the same churchyard as that brother of hers. Still, at least she weren't laid to rest in the same grave. Oh, she was adamant about that, you know.' She lightly grasped her son's arm and leaned closer. 'Why, when Angus died, Megan told me she were that happy, God forgive her, she could have danced round his grave in pure joy.'

Mark, his meal barely touched, immediately jumped up from the table, and with a muttered: 'Back in a bit,' he hurried from the cottage. He had been so stunned the night before, that only now did he remember he had left his bike beside the churchyard wall, but he was returning there for more than just the old bike.

He went through the lychgate, following the narrow winding path to where he had seen the 'Lady' finally cease her weaving and wafting about the night before, and had floated as a blanket of mist over one particular grave.

Once there, he began to tremble. The name on the headstone was Angus Lipton. His mother's words suddenly came back to him in reiteration of Megan being so happy at her brother's death, that she could have danced round his grave in pure joy.

Mark was certain it was Megan's ghost he had seen the night before, doing what she had probably not dared to do in life. As he glanced across the churchyard, he could see the fresh mound of earth where Megan had been laid to rest the day before. Mark was so disturbed, he still forgot to collect the old bike and take it home.

The following Friday evening, as was his habit, Mark met his friends, Ed and Mike, in the Black Horse. They noticed after a short while that Mark was subdued and preoccupied.

Ed could not resist teasing the placid, easy-going Mark. 'What's up with you, then?' he asked. 'Set eyes on some lass who's caught your interest, eh?'

Mark slowly smiled. 'In a way, you might say that,' he replied, refusing to be drawn further. He had been tempted to tell them about seeing the 'Lady' who he firmly believed to be the ghost of Megan Lipton, but the ensuing laughter and gossip deriving from such an admission would spread through the village like wildfire, and Mark would be the butt of cruel jokes for years to come. Wisely, he refrained from the almost aching need to discuss his experience.

Later that night, as Mark peddled home on his repaired bicycle, he did not whistle, nor did he pass the churchyard. Despite the fact that it was raining with a vengeance, the route he took was a long one and certainly not as scenic.

Nevertheless, it was worth the trouble. Mark had no wish to tempt fate. One sighting of Megan had been enough, more than enough, and though he would hold the memory like a treasured secret possession, in a kind of awed reverence, he had no wish for a repeat performance of seeing the ghost of Megan Lipton — dancing or otherwise — flitting about a moonlit churchyard, full of a morbid joy which sat ill with what was expected of one no longer mortal.

Enough To Chill The Blood

This may seem to be *the* classical case to many readers; there is a haunting to examine and a history to research, and, in truth, it is rare that we are blessed with such an ideal arrangement. All too often, a haunting is not reported because the percipient is unable to offer tangible proof of the experience: something which few if any can provide. Here, the percipient undergoes many psychological and emotional reactions to the haunting, beginning with her own mind temporarily blocking out the details of her horrific experience: a rarity, though a valid aspect of the shock experienced. Another interesting feature is that, with seemingly total disregard for the horror, and only seconds after the event, she rushed through almost the entire path of the phenomena in order to reach an area in which she considered herself safe. This case also illustrates the diligence of the investigative officers in gathering every shred of evidence available.

IN THE EARLY HOURS of the morning, Sally Rawlinson pulled her satin dressing gown more tightly around herself and swallowed a mouthful of the tea which she had just made. She could hardly stop shivering, even though the kitchen was warm, as was the rest of the house.

When Sally moved from her little flat to this end terraced house, she immediately had the house completely refurbished, using most of her savings. It was a solid house, but had been badly neglected for years. Even so, Sally was surprised that it had been on the market for so long. Granted, it was in a shocking state, but its potential was obvious, and the asking price was well below the market value.

Sally reflected that it was now seven months to the day since she moved in to her house, which she now had cause to be extremely proud of. Every room had been renovated and tastefully decorated. The kitchen, especially, gave her much satisfaction, with its fitted cupboards and work surfaces in blonde wood, and all the latest labour-saving items of equipment boldly in evidence.

As she drank the hot tea, Sally gradually felt a little easier. Really, she had been foolish to let her imagination get the better of her. She had stopped shivering now. But was still reluctant to go back to bed.

This is ridiculous, she thought. After all, what was there to be afraid of?

With trepidation, Sally started to recall what had caused her to wake up at such an ungodly hour: the kitchen clock served as an announcement that her somnolent interstice had lasted for no longer than an hour and a half. She had been peacefully sleeping in her large, elegant bedroom, with its pink, floral-papered walls, matching duvet cover and curtains, and thick, plush, beige carpet. A pretty room, a light, airy, happy room, Sally had thought it. Yet she had just run from it in terror. So shaken was she by her ordeal, that her mind wandered uncontrollably, seemingly skirting the memory of an issue to which she should have had instant access.

She recalled now how her bedroom had looked before the refurbishment. Vaguely remembering the faded, nondescript wallpaper and chipped paintwork, and a rotted sash-window frame, for the first time she wondered who had once occupied the room.

At last she won her tiring battle for concentration, and her mind quickly clicked back into gear.

Out of a deep slumber, Sally had woken. At first she had lain in bed listening intently. She could hear voices, alarmingly close to the very bed in which she lay, though she could see no one. It was a conversation between a man and a woman. Muffled, barely discernible, but giving the impression of two people roused from sleep. Next, Sally heard the heavy footsteps of a man, and creaking floorboards beside her bed. Only now did Sally question that. Her whole house was thickly carpeted, so how could she have heard footsteps? Also, she was not aware of any creaking floorboards in the house, but creak they did then, several of them, to the extent that Sally had followed their route, across her bedroom, out on the landing, and then the noise really started: the high pitched screeching cry of a very young baby, an insistent, desperate piercing, screaming cry. It grew closer and closer, making Sally think: 'He's bringing the baby in here — in *my* bedroom!'

Then, her blood ran cold as she heard a thump, and a bang, then what sounded like someone falling down the stairs and still the sound of the screeching baby. Then all at once, silence. At this point, Sally had shot from her bed and run all the way downstairs to the kitchen. Only as the fluorescent light pinged into life and bathed the room in its painful brilliance, did she heave a shuddering sigh of relief. She was safe in here. Safe? But safe from what? How could she understand and rationalise to herself what she had just experienced. All she knew for certain was that it was enough to chill her blood.

It must have been a dream, surely. Or just imagination? But she could not understand why, of all the things one could imagine, should she experience something as blatantly spine-chilling as that, whether dream or imagination! She had never in her life witnessed anything like it.

Finally, Sally spent the rest of the night on the couch in the lounge. She felt foolish for doing so, but nothing could have induced her to go back upstairs.

The following night, Sally had to force herself to sleep in her bedroom. Repeatedly, she told herself not to be silly by lying there in the dark listening for the slightest sound. She tried to think of something pleasant in a bid to stop this nonsense which festered and irritated, keeping her away from sleep.

It must have worked, because the next thing she knew, it was morning, and as Sally drew back the curtains and looked out on a fresh sunny day, she realised how foolish she had been to let a dream bother her so much. Yes, a dream. She would not allow herself to think of it as anything else.

A couple of weeks later, it had receded in her mind to the point that Sally was no longer afraid to sleep in her bedroom.

Sally led a reasonably quiet life, she loved her job as a lecturer at the local college, and on rare occasions she would have an evening out with friends. One Thursday night, some three weeks after 'The Dream', she came home very late, having been to a birthday party. It was a lot of fun, and Sally was feeling exhausted. After a cup of tea, she hurried upstairs to bed, just managing to have a quick wash before stumbling between the wonderfully cool, fresh sheets and dropping into an instant sleep.

Hours later, Sally woke up. The pale glimmer behind the curtains hinted that dawn was not far off. For a moment, Sally did not stir. An icy dread travelled her spine. Listening intently she could not discern any sound. A sense of overwhelming relief washed over her. Just as Sally was about to roll over and go back to sleep, it began: again the sleepy voices of a man and a woman, an exchange of words Sally could not make out. Then the heavy footsteps and creaking of floorboards, the screeching of the tiny baby, the creak of a door opening, *her* door, the same creaking bedroom door she had been trying to remember to buy oil for during the last few days. More footsteps, on the landing now. Louder and louder came the screaming of the baby. The thud, bump, crash, and the horrible sound of someone falling downstairs. And finally, the deathly hush.

Once more, Sally fled to the kitchen. As she drank a scalding hot cup of tea, and replayed the horrible sequence of events through her mind, she came to the realisation that if she could not manage to sort this problem out, she would go mad. She had hoped and prayed never to experience this again.

151

Sally tried to recall when it had last occurred. She checked the kitchen calendar. It was on a Thursday night. She recalled it clearly, as the next day had been a colleague's last day at college and everyone had assembled in one of the recreational lounges after work to give the departing colleague a gift. Thus, Sally could be positive about the date of the first occurrence.

She thought it significant that this too was a Thursday night, but there was a more pressing puzzle to consider. Why, after living in the house for seven months, did it start *now*? Why not a week after she moved in or a month after? *Why now*? And, would it happen again? Sally shuddered at the thought!

The next day, during her lunch time break, Sally visited her local church to make arrangements to have the house blessed. Perhaps that would put a stop to the horrible haunting, for Sally could no longer pretend to herself that it was merely a dream.

To Sally's surprise, the priest made no argument against her fears of ghostly happenings. She was truly dumbfounded when he told her he was afraid God's blessing would have little, if any effect. Apparently, both the priest and his predecessor had already tried to quieten the disturbance more than once over the years, but without success.

He recalled the last time he attended. It had scared him greatly because a baby was heard crying, as if in pain, during his ceremony of offering the house for God's protection. No trace could be found of an infant, though its cries seemed to be coming from inside the staircase. It required all his will to continue the ceremony, and only on its completion did the frantic cries stop. He could not explain how, but he knew his task had been unsuccessful.

While the priest himself could do nothing to help Sally, he asked if he might contact another priest who had experience of exorcism. Sally agreed, and so arrangements were made and a service of exorcism duly performed.

For one glorious month afterwards, Sally was grateful that she experienced only a blissful peace in the house. She loved her home, and hated the thought of being driven from it because of living in dread of the ghastly disturbance happening again.

But happen again it did.

One Friday night in August, Sally had a guest staying overnight. Carol worked at the same college as Sally. They both enjoyed hiking whenever they got the chance, and planned to set off early the next morning to walk the Cumbrian fells around Kendal, taking with them provisions to last the day. Carol was spending the night at Sally's home so that they could make an early start.

This time, when Sally awoke in the early hours from the depths of sleep, she knew what to expect, but still, it made her blood run cold. She huddled under the duvet cover and cringed as the voices violated her will, then came the footsteps and creaking floorboards, and the screaming baby, the crying growing louder and louder as the man seemed to be returning. Then came the chilling thud, crash, bump which ended in the familiar, ultimate silence.

The moment it was over, Sally hurried from her bedroom to again seek the reassuring comfort of the kitchen, and out on the landing she came face to face with Carol.

Carol looked terrified. '*My God*! Whatever was *that*?' she begged.

Sally felt only mildly relieved that Carol had heard it too, and she encouraged her friend to go down to the kitchen with her, where, over a cup of strong tea she would explain everything; or at least, as much as she was able to.

It was such a solace finally to have someone to share this with, as she had told no one before — other than the parish priest — because she was fearful of being ridiculed.

As it transpired, Carol understood only too well what Sally must have gone through, having been a witness to it herself, and after recovering her own senses, she was able to offer some comfort to her friend.

Sally was pleasantly surprised and reassured by her friend's supportive attitude, and asked Carol's opinion about contacting the parish priest again, after all, there was not exactly an abundance of choices.

But Carol suggested, instead, that they discuss the matter with her friend, Richard, from The Institute for Psychical Research.

Sally was doubtful at first, having read several times of psychic researchers seeming to form their conclusions purely on the basis of whether or not the same events occur during their one night's vigil. At least the clergy were not as prone to make judgements of such magnitude.

Carol agreed that it would be a waste of time waiting for a group of austere individuals to pass judgement, when they were both intelligent enough to know it was not a figment of imagination that brought them downstairs in the middle of the night. And considering the phenomena had not occurred during the previous month, the odds were stacked heavily against a repetition on that one particular night at the group's convenience, and could only suggest the foregone conclusion being that they were both utterly insane. Carol ended her argument by stating that there was already enough evidence to suggest a genuine haunting, but while the priest was in agreement about this, it now required someone with adequate training in such matters.

And so the two young women approached Richard, who promptly set the wheels in motion.

A significant portion of the resulting action consisted of tracing fourteen of the previous owners, spanning almost twenty years in the history of the house and taking investigators all over Britain during the next thirteen months, the purpose being to establish when the haunting first started.

Meanwhile, equipment set up in Sally's home revealed three more occurrences of the phenomena, spread over a period of seven weeks: two on the night of Thursday/Friday, one on the night of Wednesday/Thursday. The phenomena then ceased. Whether the cessation was temporary or permanent could not be established at this stage: it just failed to happen during a period of three months. A sporadic repetitive occurrence is notorious for announcing its beginning by a sudden manifestation; while the end of its cycle, and even its existence, is indicated more subtly by a complete failure to manifest.

By now though, reports coming in from the travelling investigators were building a clear picture of the phenomena having an annual cycle. It was also claimed to be the one reason why so many residents sold the terraced house.

Sally's home was promptly exorcised, although the search to find the first occurrence of the phenomena continued for a further ten months, one previous owner being interviewed after another, before arriving at the door of a very astonished Mrs T., who held all the relevant answers to the lengthy though informative quest.

Mrs T., currently married to her second husband and with two teenage children, remembered only too well the initial cause of the phenomena, which had taken place nearly twenty years earlier. She was able now to speak with detachment, and admittedly she had only bad memories of the terraced house.

She had been eight months pregnant when her first husband's work had taken them to the area. They both liked the end terraced house and had great plans for it, though none were realised.

Brian was very attentive, both throughout the pregnancy and after their son was born. It had been hard during those first few months and Brian had awoken virtually every time, when the baby cried in the night.

Having such a ravenous son soon took its toll, as Brian would be so tired he frequently slept right through the alarm after waking up six or seven times during the night. Consequently, he was late for work more often than not, and this created further stress which was significantly compounded by the nightly interruptions. The baby slept in the bedroom furthest away from their own, but his cry was loud enough to wake half the street, and Brian and herself suffered terribly from the effects of such a demanding baby. It was a miracle if two hours went by without him needing a feed. Mrs T. intended only to breast feed her son, but was forced to include a bottle and mashed rusks into the feeds.

By the time their son reached one month of age, both Brian and herself were exhausted and barely had the strength to struggle out of bed to feed the baby. Mrs T. praised Brian for his support, as they often shared the task between them. She was grateful for his help, because there were many nights when she would have given anything for someone else to take over the feeding ritual. Brian had told her that he may as well help, as he would have had difficulty getting back to sleep anyway.

The baby was just approaching ten weeks old when Brian and herself awoke for about the third time that night. It was Mrs T's turn to feed their son, but Brian, seeing how exhausted she was, volunteered to make another bottle and told her to try to sleep.

Mrs T. then fell immediately into a light doze, through which she could hear the creaking floorboards as Brian went to collect the baby. He was walking back along the landing towards the top of the stairs when Mrs T. heard such a terrible crashing noise that it woke her from the doze and she sat up in bed listening now only to a deathly silence.

She was not sure how much time had elapsed since Brian went to feed the baby, but she was puzzled because Brian was not in bed beside her and there was no sound from the baby. Usually, her son would cry occasionally when having a bottle, as if in objection to not having the comfort of his mother's breast.

She rose sleepily from the bed and fumbled for her dressing gown, then she heard a noise on the stairs and a moment later Brian hobbled into the bedroom with the terrible news. The baby had brought up his feed and Brian was carrying him downstairs to clean and change him. But in his tiredness, he had lost his footing at the top of the stairs and crashed down them with the baby. He told her he had phoned for an ambulance, but there was no rush. Their son was dead.

Brian never forgave himself for what had happened and a little over a year later, he ended his torment by taking his own life. Mrs T., having suffered the loss of both her son and her husband, desperately needed to get far away from all the constant reminders, and so, putting the terraced house up for sale, she moved halfway across the country to a rented flat.

Later, she met and married her current husband, Mr T., and has since led a charmed life in comparison with her previous existence. Their two beautiful children have helped to ease her pain, and the elegant lifestyle of a secluded, modern, detached bungalow with an acre of land, her own car, dinner parties, two holidays each year and lots of friends have contributed to making her earlier experience in an end terraced house in an unfamiliar town seem as if it had all taken place in a completely different lifetime.

Many of the investigators' questions were answered during the course of Mrs T's story and there was not the slightest doubt that this information explained the cause of the haunting. The timing of it, however, was difficult to assimilate in relation to either the date of the baby's death or of Brian's because the phenomena occurred so irregularly. The strength of the testimony from past owners of the property substantiated that the ghostly noises could be heard around July, August and September, though the actual dates of manifestation were not as easily remembered as the inherent need to vacate the house as quickly as possible.

From the dates supplied by both Sally and Mrs T., it can only be said that the phenomena occurred at sporadic intervals during a three-month period between the date of the baby's death and that of his father, Brian.

Sally is now content to live in the home she loves, but the memory of such chilling phenomena will obviously still haunt her, as it will Mrs. T. and thirteen other previous owners of the house.

A Touch Of Old London

This is an old favourite of mine for many reasons. One reason is that the bridge itself illustrates aspects of the supernatural on a normal, everyday level. Most onlookers at the site have described it as a physical impossibility, yet it stands before their very eyes in its splendid reality. It can be touched and seen by day and by night, it can be examined and inspected until one is absolutely sure it is really there, yet within an hour of leaving, most find themselves questioning its reality. Some will even turn back to reassure themselves they were not dreaming. And this is only the bridge! It is perhaps fitting that such a 'physical impossibility' is haunted, and that it was reported for the same reason that so many hauntings are, out of a sense of duty, a seemingly mundane quality which has enabled parascience to help millions of people over the years. The case also describes one of few sites where the amateur ghosthunter can enjoy comfort and modern conveniences, without invading anyone's privacy, and these are the reasons why directions to the site have also been included.

In 1962, when the City of London, England, found that the famous London Bridge really was 'falling down', they decided to put it up for sale.

The old bridge was sinking into the River Thames because of the increasing weight of the traffic. During its life, it had served millions of Londoners; though it was still a shock to many Britons when they heard it was to be sold.

An equal, or perhaps even greater shock hit the American population when they learned that Arizona developer, Robert McCulloch had bought the bridge, and that he intended transporting it from England to the southwestern United States, to its new site in the middle of the Arizona desert.

The vision of London Bridge sitting out in the vast expanse of desert sand was at first, the most ludicrous thing anyone could think of, but Robert McCulloch was not to be dissuaded by overwhelming public opinion. He was a man of courage and determination, and he knew exactly what he was doing.

The bridge was subsequently taken apart, stone by stone, each stone being numbered and coded. It was then shipped sixteen thousand kilometres to Long Beach, California, then trucked to Lake Havasu City, Arizona.

Under the direction of Robert Beresford, a young Nottingham civil engineer, reconstruction of the bridge began on September 23rd, 1968, with the laying of the cornerstone by Sir Gilbert Inglefield, then Lord Mayor of London. Finally, the bridge was completed and, probably to the relief of many observers, a long channel was dredged under the bridge to divert water from Lake Havasu. London Bridge was officially dedicated and opened on October 10th, 1971, by the then Lord Mayor of London, Sir Peter Studd, in the presence of Jack Williams, Governor of Arizona.

London Bridge does not stand alone though, because an English Village was built beside the bridge to make its authenticity stand proud. Little touches were also exported from the United Kingdom, like English grass, a double decker bus, a red telephone kiosk, and the old, faithful, London taxi. The scene was completed with an English restaurant, The City of London Arms, and of course the English pub, Ye Hog in Armour.

The English Village and London Bridge are now two of the most charming tourist attractions in the southwestern United States, thanks to Robert McCulloch, of the chainsaw fame, who paid $2.5 million for the pleasure of tourists throughout the world who wish to partake of the splendour of his genius in the middle of the Arizona desert. The original idea must have seemed ludicrous to a great many people, on both sides of the Atlantic, but the superb reality of Robert's intent cannot be denied. One only needs to ask the name of the founder of Lake Havasu City, or who provided the very desirable acre of land on which to build. And there is not even an admission fee.

Patti Berenson was one of the many people to wonder at this engineering masterpiece. It was like an impossible dream, standing irrefutably before her. She was not alone in feeling the magic of October 1971, nor was she the only person to walk along the promenade under London Bridge, or walk across the bridge and back several times sporting a look of wonderment.

Patti was also not alone when she remarked about her elated surprise at seeing the four ghosts in Victorian dress, walking across London Bridge. They seemed so real in their transparency, that she could not understand how the effect was obtained, but it was a marvellous finishing touch for the organisers to think of creating such realistic London ghosts.

Her only problem was, she could find no one to answer her questions about the ghosts. The more she asked, the more she encouraged other curious onlookers. Before long, there was a small crowd of them, searching the sky and the roofs of the village buildings for the light of a projector. There was none to be found, and it was not long before it became painfully evident that these four ghosts were not part of the scheduled show: they were *real!*

Since 1971, others too have seen ghosts casually strolling across the bridge, the most frequent reports being of a man and a woman in Victorian dress, as if they were taking an evening stroll, apparently oblivious to the arid desert around them.

No one knows how many ghosts abound, or even if the same ghosts have been seen more than once. Usually, the sightings are made by startled percipients while walking on the promenade below the bridge, and those who have dared to take a closer look, have so far been disappointed to find the ghosts gone by the time they reached the bridge. Thus, all the lengthy sightings have been from a distance.

Some closer encounters have also been reported. A percipient standing on the bridge admiring the view, has often been bumped into by an invisible entity. Some have even seen the ghosts immediately after this contact, but only for a fraction of a second.

The ghosts still walk on London Bridge to this day, and it is certainly worth a visit if one is in the area. Lake Havasu City is located on State Highway 95, alongside the Colorado River in western Arizona, where countless British ghosts seem to have adapted well to their new life as a 'marvellous finishing touch' to an English village in the southwestern desert of the United States.